MARVEL

HEROES &
VILLAINS

MARVEL

HEROES &
VILLAINS

A journal by Nick Fury

A STUDIO PRESS BOOK

First published in the UK in 2020 by Studio Press,
an imprint of Bonnier Books UK,
The Plaza, 535 King's Road, London SW10 0SZ
Owned by Bonnier Books,
Sveavägen 56, Stockholm, Sweden

www.studiopressbooks.co.uk

www.bonnierbooks.co.uk

1 3 5 7 9 10 8 6 4 2

ISBN 978-1-78741-704-5

Written by Ned Hartley

Edited by Stephanie Milton

Designed by Rob Ward

A CIP catalogue for this book is available from the British Library

Printed and bound in China

CONTENTS

NICK FURY'S NOTES

FROM THE DESK OF NICK FURY, STRATEGIC HOMELAND INTERVENTION, ENFORCEMENT, AND LOGISTICS DIVISION, DIRECTOR

If you can fly, read minds, stick to walls or shoot laser beams out of your eyes then I've got a file on you somewhere. Probably more than one file. This is a dangerous world, after all.

When I joined S.H.I.E.L.D. I was following my father's footsteps, and I became an agent in the largest espionage agency the world has ever seen. I've been shot at, blown up, poisoned and I've even lost an eye.

You don't survive as a S.H.I.E.L.D. agent by taking anything for granted, so I've made sure that I have backups all over the world. I've had my computer systems hacked and compromised enough times to know that I can't rely on keeping one set of files in one place, so if you're reading this then you have got your hands on a hard copy of my files.

These aren't my complete files on everyone in the universe — there isn't enough space for that. This is a top-level report of all the biggest heavy-hitters, all the important heroes and villains that need to be monitored. If there's a major super-powered event somewhere on Earth then it's almost certain that somebody in these files will be involved.

You're probably asking yourself something along the lines of 'Why does Nick Fury need these files?' and 'How did he get all this information?' But here is a better question to ask yourself:

'What is Nick Fury going to do when he finds out that I have been reading his files?'

Nick Fury Jr

Nick Fury Jr

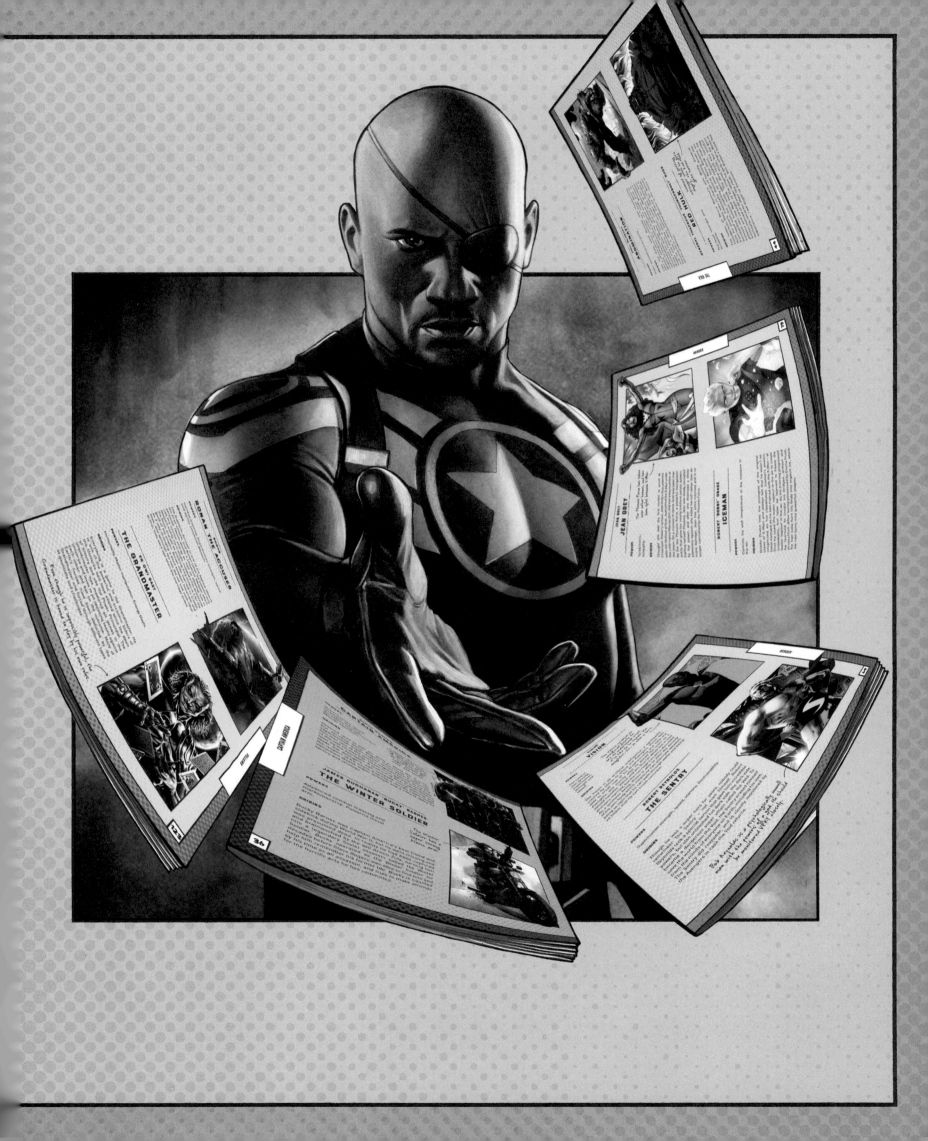

ASTRAL PROJECTION

Moving your spirit outside your body to travel in the Astral Realm.

ACOUSTIKINESIS

Manipulating and using sound using only your mind.

BIOELECTRICITY

Generation of electrical charges inside the body.

CHAOS MAGIC

A powerful branch of magic that is not fully understood.

COSMIC AWARENESS

Understanding and manipulating the building blocks of the universe.

CYBERPATHY

Talking to and manipulating technological systems using only your mind.

DIMENSIONAL TRAVEL

The ability to move between different alternate realities.

ELECTROKINESIS

Storing and controlling electricity in your body.

EMPATHY

The ability to read other people's feelings.

ENERGY BLASTS

Creating an expulsion of powerful forces from your body.

ENERGY MANIPULATION

The ability to internalise and redirect forms of energy.

FLIGHT

The ability to move through the air by your own power.

FORCE FIELD CREATION

Making energy-based barriers to protect yourself and/or others.

GEOKINESIS

The ability to control earth, rock and soil using only your mind.

GRAVIKINESIS

The control of gravity, either your own or other people's.

HEALING FACTOR

Being able to heal from wounds more quickly than a human.

SUPER POWERS

HYDROKINESIS

Control of water and the moisture in the air.

IMMORTALITY

Will not die from old age. Some immortals can be killed by other methods.

INTANGIBILITY

Can move through solid objects.

INVISIBILITY

Cannot be seen by the human eye.

MAGIC

The use of mystical arts.

OMNIPOTENCE

Vast, but not always unlimited power.

OMNISCIENCE

Vast, but not always unlimited knowledge.

POWER COSMIC

A near immeasurable power that has been mastered by Galactus.

PYROKINESIS

The ability to control, but not generate, fire using your mind.

REALITY WARPING

Changing the very nature of existence itself.

SHAPESHIFTING

Manipulation of the physical form of your body.

SUPERHUMAN DURABILITY

Being tougher and able to take more damage than humans.

SUPERHUMAN SPEED

Faster than the upper human limits.

SUPERHUMAN STRENGTH

Being able to punch harder and lift more than humans.

TELEKINESIS

The ability to move objects using your mind.

TELEPATHY

The ability to read other people's minds.

TELEPORTATION

Moving instantly from one place in space to another.

TRICHOKINESIS

Control of prehensile hair.

CHAPTER ONE
SPIDER-MAN

NICK FURY'S NOTES

I don't know what it is about Spider-Man, but the poor guy never seems to have it easy. Peter Parker's had a hard life – his parents died when he was young, and his Uncle Ben died not long after Peter gained his powers. As Spider-Man he's got more villains that are trying to kill him than any other super hero I know.

Still, there's something about Spider-Man that inspires people. Seems like every time I turn around there's a new hero with webs, swinging around New York City. It's almost getting to the point where I can't keep track of them all.

Almost.

PETER PARKER
SPIDER-MAN

POWERS

Increased strength, reflexes, stamina and agility. Sticks to walls. Wrist-mounted mechanical web-shooters. Spider-sense warns of danger.

ORIGINS

Poor Peter Parker just can't seem to catch a break. As a teenager he was bitten by a radioactive spider, which gave him the proportional strength and agility of a spider. When a robber that he let escape killed his Uncle Ben, Peter realised that with great power comes great responsibility and became a super hero. He's been an Avenger and has saved the world (and New York) more times than we can repay.

Spider-Man swings through New York using a webbing formula of his own invention.

GWEN STACY
GHOST-SPIDER

POWERS

Increased strength, reflexes, stamina and agility. Sticks to walls. Wrist-mounted mechanical web-shooters. Spider-sense warns of danger.

ORIGINS

This version of Gwen Stacy comes from a different dimension, where she was the one who was bitten by a radioactive spider instead of her boyfriend Peter Parker. In our dimension Gwen was killed by the Green Goblin, but this version of Gwen fights crime as Ghost-Spider. Gwen's father is Captain George Stacy of the NYPD and he does not approve of her career as a superhero. Gwen has had about as much bad luck as our Peter Parker, but just like our Spider-Man, she's strong, brave and determined to do the right thing.

JESSICA DREW
SPIDER-WOMAN

POWERS

Increased strength, reflexes, stamina and agility. Spider-sense warns of danger. Sticks to walls. Wrist-mounted mechanical web shooters.

ORIGINS

Jessica Drew's scientist parents used unorthodox methods to cure her uranium poisoning – they injected her with a spider-based serum and then placed her in a hibernation chamber for years. When she emerged she had new, spider-based powers. Jessica was trained to be a spy by the evil organisation Hydra, but rebelled and became the hero Spider-Woman, helping S.H.I.E.L.D. to take down criminals all over the world. Spider-Woman is not related to Spider-Man, but they were both Avengers at the same time and remain good friends.

BEN REILLY
THE SCARLET SPIDER

POWERS

Increased strength, reflexes, stamina and agility. Spider-sense warns of danger. Sticks to walls. Wrist-mounted web-shooters.

Ben once took over Peter's duties as Spidey, but he is not the hero that Peter is.

ORIGINS

A long time ago Peter Parker was cloned by the Jackal. Ben Reilly is that clone – he has all of Peter's abilities and a copy of his memories. For a long time Ben thought that he was the original and Peter was the clone, and Ben had a hard time coming to terms with the fact that he is not the original Spider-Man. Ben has tried to create a life for himself and has taken the identity of the Scarlet Spider – he has become a dark, mirror version of Spider-Man, always looking for redemption.

NORMAN OSBORN
THE GREEN GOBLIN

POWERS

Superhuman strength, stamina, reflexes, agility and healing.

Norman Osborn bonded with the Carnage symbiote, calling himself the Red Goblin.

ORIGINS

The father of Peter Parker's childhood friend Harry Osborn, Norman Osborn (aka the Green Goblin) is perhaps Spider-Man's greatest nemesis. Businessman Norman Osborn was the head of Oscorp industries and he created the Green Goblin identity so he could run organised crime in New York City. Osborn fought Spider-Man regularly and killed his girlfriend Gwen Stacy. Norman Osborn is brilliantly clever and utterly ruthless – a very dangerous combination. However, Osborn's narcissism and constant craving for power is almost always the cause of his downfall.

HARRY OSBORN
THE GREEN GOBLIN

POWERS

Superhuman strength, stamina, reflexes, agility and healing.

ORIGINS

Harry Osborn was Peter Parker's first friend. At first he really didn't know that his best friend was Spider-Man and his father was the Green Goblin. Harry saw his father die (in fact Norman survived) in a battle with Spider-Man and took on the Green Goblin identity during a massive psychological breakdown. Harry has had troubles with addiction and drugs, and used the Green Goblin suit as a way to deal with them. Harry has since recovered and gone to therapy, and now he is determined to do the right thing and to redeem the Osborn name, no matter what his father does.

DR OTTO OCTAVIUS
DOCTOR OCTOPUS

POWERS

Can mentally control powerful metal arms.

ORIGINS

A scientific genius, Dr Otto Octavius was driven mad when an accident with radiation fused his mechanical metal arms to his body. Octavius, who was always smug and arrogant, became a super villain. He started calling himself Doctor Octopus then upgraded his limbs and used them for a life of crime. Doctor Octopus sees Spider-Man as his nemesis. Even though they are both superior scientists, Spider-Man is seen as a hero, while Doctor Octopus is a villain.

Doctor Otto Octavius has moved his consciousness between cloned bodies, and once took over Spider-Man's body, becoming the Superior Spider-Man.

MAX DILLLON
ELECTRO

POWERS

Electricity storage and manipulation.

ORIGINS

Electrical engineer Max Dillon was hit by lightning while repairing a power line. Instead of killing him, it turned him into a living capacitor, giving him the power to store and control electricity. Electro immediately became a professional criminal, using his powers to steal, threaten and kidnap. Dillon has fought Spider-Man on countless occasions, and despite Electro's amazing power levels he often loses because he is outsmarted by the wall-crawler. Electro is a member of the Sinister Six, a fluid group of super villains who have teamed up (unsuccessfully) several times to take down Spider-Man.

CLETUS KASADY
CARNAGE

POWERS

Suit gives him super strength, stamina and agility, and allows him to change shape.

Cletus Kasady seems to be impossible to kill, and has been resurrected from the dead by his followers.

ORIGINS

Cletus Kasady was a serial killer, and is pretty much the worst person in the world to get a powerful alien super suit. Unfortunately when the Venom costume produced offspring it bonded with Kasady, and he became the super villain known as Carnage. Carnage is a psychotic killer – he has no moral code and revels in death and destruction. Kasady seems to have permanently bonded with his suit, and it is now part of his bloodstream. Kasady should not be underestimated – he is intelligent and charismatic, and can manipulate large groups of people.

ADRIAN TOOMES
VULTURE

POWERS

Flight harness allows him to fly and gives him super strength.

ORIGINS

A talented inventor, Adrian Toomes created a flight harness that allowed him to soar through the sky. After he was cheated by his business partner he used the suit to rob and steal throughout New York. Spider-Man stopped him and the two have been enemies ever since. The Vulture is a killer and holds a special grudge against Spider-Man – he has been part of several versions of the Sinister Six. The Vulture is constantly upgrading his flight suit and can even use it to affect the gravity of things around him.

SERGEI KRAVINOFF
KRAVEN THE HUNTER

POWERS

Enhanced stamina, strength and reflexes.

Kraven once buried Spider-Man alive as part of his macabre 'Last Hunt'. →

ORIGINS

Kraven is the son of a Russian aristocrat, who wanted to prove that he was the greatest big game hunter by killing the hardest target imaginable – Spider-Man! Kraven got his powers from a potion that slows the ageing process and gives him strength and stamina, and has nearly killed Spidey on more than one occasion. Kraven enjoys teaming up with other villains to fight Spidey, including his half-brother Dmitri Smerdyakov, the Chameleon. Several of Kraven's children have followed in his footsteps in trying to hunt down Spider-Man.

DMITRI SMERDYAKOV
CHAMELEON

POWERS

Can take on the appearance of any person at will.

ORIGINS

The master of disguise, the Russian-born Chameleon is the half-brother of Kraven the Hunter. A soviet spy, the Chameleon initially used make-up and prosthetics to change his appearance, but later had surgical and chemical enhancements that allow him to change his appearance at will. Dmitri is no longer a spy, and is now a criminal, using his powers of disguise for personal gain. The Chameleon is ruthless, and years of impersonating other people have been incredibly damaging to his mental health, driving him quite insane.

FELICIA HARDY
BLACK CAT

POWERS

Incredible training and reflexes. 'Bad luck' power.

Black Cat is heavily involved in the New York criminal underworld.

ORIGINS

Black Cat has been both a hero and a villain at different times in her career, depending on how much influence Spider-Man has on her at the time. Felicia Hardy is the daughter of a cat burglar, and she trained herself in martial arts and acrobatics so that she, too, could become an agile thief. She initially fought Spider-Man, but then she reformed and briefly dated him. They split up because she preferred Spider-Man to Peter Parker, but the two are still friends. Black Cat's power affects probability – people around her always have the worst luck!

EDDIE BROCK
VENOM

POWERS

His suit gives him super strength, stamina and agility, and allows him to change shape.

ORIGINS

Eddie Brock gets his powers from an alien symbiote, which was originally brought to Earth to be Spider-Man's costume. When Spider-Man split from the costume it resented him, and bonded with Eddie. Venom's main motivation is hatred of Spider-Man, but he does have his own sense of morality, and tries to help the innocent when he can. The suit is especially vulnerable to fire and loud noises, both of which Spider-Man has used to his advantage in the past.

The Venom suit has been worn by Flash Thompson, Scorpion and even Deadpool.

MIGUEL O'HARA
SPIDER-MAN 2099

POWERS

Superhuman strength, agility and stamina. Talons in fingers and toes.

ORIGINS

Miguel is from the future, though possibly not our future – in his version of the year 2099 there are no more heroes, and the world is run by heartless corporations. Miguel was in an accident that rewrote half his DNA with a spider's genetic code, giving him incredible powers. Miguel knew of the original Spider-Man from his history books, and so took his name to carry on the Spider-Man legacy. Spider-Man 2099 has travelled to the present day and met Peter Parker several times, but his real home is in the year 2099, fighting the evil Alchemax corporation.

CINDY MOON
SILK

POWERS

Increased strength, reflexes, stamina and agility. Organic webshooters. Sticks to walls.

ORIGINS

Cindy Moon was bitten by the same radioactive spider as Peter Parker and was given similar, but not identical, powers. After training to use her powers, Cindy was locked in a bunker for years to protect her from Morlun and the Inheritors – psychic vampires who want to consume anyone with spider powers. Spider-Man eventually found Cindy and brought her into the world. As the costumed hero Silk she finds it hard to navigate the world that she was locked away from, and is always wary of another attack from Morlun and his family.

ALEKSEI SYSTEVICH
RHINO

POWERS

Superhuman strength, endurance and durability. Damage resistant suit.

The Rhino is permanently bonded to his powerful armour.

ORIGINS

Rhino might not be Spider-Man's smartest villain, but he's definitely one of the toughest. A street thug who volunteered for an experimental procedure, Aleksei Systevich bonded with an artificial skin suit which gave him incredible levels of strength. As the Rhino, he used this strength to embark on a life of crime, often clashing with Spider-Man. The fact that his other regular fight partner is the Hulk reveals a lot about the Rhino's power levels. The Rhino loves to charge at his enemies with his augmented rhino horn, and Spidey uses the Rhino's impatience and inertia against him.

MARTIN LI
MISTER NEGATIVE

POWERS

Darkforce energy gives him super strength and allows him to 'corrupt' people.

ORIGINS

Mister Negative lives two lives – the kind-hearted Martin Li transforms into villainous New York crime lord Mister Negative. His two sides do not seem to acknowledge each other even though they share the same body. Mister Negative can use extradimensional Darkforce energy to corrupt people and control them, even briefly turning Spider-Man evil when he touched him. Just as Mister Negative corrupts people, Martin Li can sometimes heal people, and he was able to heal Eddie Brock when he was nearly dying.

MACDONALD 'MAC' GARGAN
SCORPION

POWERS

Super strength, endurance, speed.

ORIGINS

Private Investigator Mac Gargan was paid by Daily Bugle publisher J Jonah Jameson to be the subject of a risky experiment. The experiment would give him the powers of a scorpion, so that he could defeat Spider-Man. Gargan was permanently fused with his scorpion suit and mechanical tail, and he blamed Jameson (and Spider-Man) for what had happened. The Scorpion suit has been upgraded through the years, and Gargan even spent some time with the Venom symbiote suit before returning to his identity as Scorpion.

Gargan hates Jameson as much as he hates Spider-Man.

WILLIAM BAKER AKA FLINT MARKO
SANDMAN

POWERS

Molecular structure made of sand.

ORIGINS

Whilst on the run from the law, Flint Marko hid in an atomic testing site where he was bombarded with radiation, fusing his body with the sand of the site. Afterwards, Marko found that he could convert his body to sand and manipulate it at will. Taking the name Sandman, he continued his criminal activities but was stopped by Spider-Man who first beat him by using a vacuum cleaner to contain his sand-like body. Sandman has returned countless times to battle Spider-Man, and his shifting structure makes him very strong.

QUENTIN BECK
MYSTERIO

POWERS

Master illusionist.

Caution: Nothing is quite as it seems when dealing with Quentin Beck.

ORIGINS

Special effects artist Quentin Beck used his knowledge of illusion and deception to commit crimes, and framed Spider-Man for robbery. Spider-Man was able to clear his name, and Mysterio blamed him for ruining his career, then joined the Sinister Six. Mysterio is a master of illusion and his suit contains advanced technology including holographic projectors, canisters of hallucinogenic gas and incredibly strong magnets. He combines his weapons to create illusions that seem completely real to anyone caught in his spell, but he does not usually use sorcery or real magic like Doctor Strange.

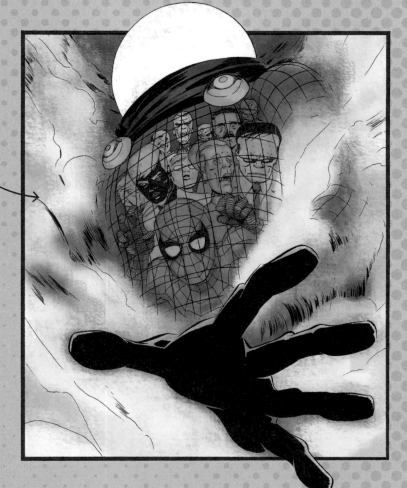

DR CURTIS CONNORS
LIZARD

POWERS

Super strength, healing and endurance.
Some telepathy with reptiles.

ORIGINS

Doctor Curtis Connors was a gifted surgeon who became obsessed with finding a way to regrow his lost arm. Connors created an experimental serum based on reptilian DNA. When he took it his arm grew back, but he was transformed into a rampaging lizard creature. The Lizard is a devious super villain who wants to turn every human in the world into a super-reptile like himself. Curt Connors is devastated by the actions he takes as the Lizard, and Spider-Man has regularly helped to change him back from his lizard form to being a human once again.

JASON MACENDALE, NED LEEDS, RODERICK KINGSLEY AND PHIL URICH
HOBGOBLIN

POWERS

Advanced weaponry including pumpkin bombs, a glider and blasters.

ORIGINS

The first Hobgoblin was billionaire Roderick Kingsley who created the villain to taunt Spider-Man. Several people have worn the costume, including Peter Parker's friend Ned Leeds, who was brainwashed by Kingsley. For years the Hobgoblin identity was used by Jason Macendale, a former CIA agent turned super villain, before being taken on by Daily Bugle reporter Ben Urich's nephew, Phil Urich. No matter who wears the suit, the weapons, glider, taunting laugh and hatred of Spider-Man are the same.

The Hobgoblin is clearly inspired by the Green Goblin, and is just as dangerous.

MILES WARREN
JACKAL

POWERS

Enhanced strength and speed. Genius-level scientist.

ORIGINS

Miles Warren was Peter Parker's biology professor at Empire State University. Warren became obsessed with Peter's girlfriend Gwen Stacy, and after Gwen died, Miles blamed Spider-Man, then took on the costumed alter-ego of the Jackal. Warren used his knowledge of genetics to clone Peter Parker and Gwen Stacy several times, with varying levels of stability. Miles Warren has also altered his own DNA to give himself the strength, speed and agility of a jackal, but this has turned him into a monstrous version of the man that he once was.

UNKNOWN
MORLUN

POWERS

Superhuman strength, stamina. Life absorption touch.

ORIGINS

Morlun and his family are psychic vampires who have roamed the multiverse for centuries. They feed from animal 'totems' who get their powers from animals, like Spider-Man. Morlun is stronger and more dangerous than any foe that Spider-Man has ever fought, and Peter Parker has only been able to defeat him by bringing together different versions of Spider-Man from different dimensions. The Spider heroes beat Morlun and his family, the Inheritors, but it seems that it is impossible to destroy Morlun for good.

Morlun and his family have killed many different versions of Spider-Man from different realities.

ALISTAIR SMYTHE
THE ULTIMATE
SPIDER-SLAYER

POWERS

Superhuman strength, speed, stamina. Cybernetics expert. Blades/talons.

ORIGINS

Alistair Smythe's father, Spencer Smythe, created a series of deadly robots called the Spider-Slayers, designed to kill Spider-Man. When Spencer died Alistair took over the family legacy of Spider-Man hatred. Alistair once used a wheelchair, but wears a carapace of body armour to make himself faster, stronger and pointier than a normal human. As well as being physically powerful, Smythe controls a small army of deadly Spider-Slayer robots, which he updates with bleeding edge technology.

LONNIE LINCOLN

TOMBSTONE

POWERS

Superhuman strength, agility and durability. Razor-sharp teeth.

Tombstone has a trademark low growl, which can make him hard to understand.

ORIGINS

Albino mobster Lonnie Lincoln worked for years as a button man for a New York criminal family. His pale skin, whisper-quiet voice and teeth filed to sharp points made him one of the most intimidating figures in the criminal underworld. Tombstone was an effective enforcer before he got super powers, but exposure to an experimental gas gave him increased strength and made him resistant to injury. With this added power, Tombstone has set his sights on becoming the king of New York.

UNKNOWN

HAMMERHEAD

POWERS

Incredibly strong, metal-laced head.

ORIGINS

Once a street-level enforcer for a New York crime family, Hammerhead's head was damaged in a severe gangland beating. Instead of simply healing him, his surgeon gave him a flattened, unbreakable head. Hammerhead is a major player in the New York underworld, and has moved between various crime families as his ambition has grown. Hammerhead's head is now reinforced with Vibranium, and his signature move is charging an opponent head-first, like a bull. His head is so strong that he can break through walls without hurting himself.

VILLAINS

CHAPTER TWO
IRON MAN

NICK FURY'S NOTES

For someone who acts like he can solve any problem on his own (with the right technology), Tony Stark seems to keep a lot of people around him. Tony's problem is that he's always trying to fix things, even when they aren't broken, and that can be dangerous when it's taken too far.

I'm glad that Tony has people like Rhodey and Pepper around to ground him and keep him in check. What happened to Happy Hogan was a tragedy – by all accounts he was a good man.

TONY STARK
IRON MAN

POWERS

Genius-level inventor. Super-humanly powerful suit of armour.

Tony Stark is the head of Stark Industries, and his inventions are known as Stark Tech.

ORIGINS

Billionaire industrialist inventor Tony Stark was caught in an explosion which lodged a piece of shrapnel dangerously close to his heart. Captured by terrorists, Tony Stark was ordered to build weapons, but instead created an iron suit of armour to make his escape. Tony is now Iron Man, the armoured Avenger who uses advanced technology to power his state-of-the-art suit. The only thing that matches Tony's confidence is his heroism, and he acts as an inspiration for super heroes all over the world. There is no problem in the world that Tony Stark cannot think his way out of.

JAMES 'RHODEY' RHODES
WAR MACHINE

POWERS

Military training. Suit of technologically-advanced armour. Weapons.

ORIGINS

James Rhodes and Tony Stark have been best friends ever since Iron Man rescued Rhodey after a plane crash. The War Machine suit is a modified version of the Iron Man armour that was created just for Rhodey, and it is packed full of some of the most advanced and powerful weapons ever seen. War Machine is a better team player than Iron Man. He's worked successfully alongside S.H.I.E.L.D. and the US army as well as the Avengers.

VIRGINIA 'PEPPER' POTTS
RESCUE

POWERS

Suit of technologically-advanced armour.

ORIGINS

Pepper first came to Tony Stark's attention when she was a low-level employee who pointed out an accounting error that he'd made. Rather than get angry, Tony promoted Pepper and gradually gave her more and more control over the company. Now she runs Stark Industries so that Tony has time to be a billionaire playboy super hero. Pepper and Tony have a complicated relationship, both professionally and romantically. When necessary, Pepper pilots a Stark suit, adopting the super-hero name "Rescue" and using Stark technology to help those in need.

Pepper and Tony have a complicated relationship, but he trusts her completely.

HAROLD 'HAPPY' HOGAN
HAPPY HOGAN

POWERS

Combat training.

ORIGINS

Happy Hogan got his nickname when he was a boxer, because of his refusal to smile when he was in the ring. He was Tony Stark's bodyguard and chauffeur while Iron Man had a secret identity. Before Stark went public with the knowledge that he was Iron Man, Happy often wore the Iron Man armour as part of elaborate ruses to protect Tony's identity. Happy was a brave and loyal man who would do anything for his boss, and he died protecting Tony Stark during a battle with Spymaster.

UNKNOWN
MANDARIN

POWERS

Superhumanly skilled in martial arts. Each of his ten rings has different powers.

ORIGINS

Iron Man's greatest enemy uses ten power rings that he adapted from a crashed alien space ship. Each ring has a different power and the Mandarin can control them psychically. The Mandarin uses his power to rule over the inhabitants of the Valley of Spirits in mainland China. He is a vicious tyrant bent on world domination, and his rings make him more than a match for Iron Man's most powerful suits of armour.

The Mandarin is incredibly powerful, and will stop at nothing to crush Iron Man.

BORIS BULLSKI
TITANIUM MAN

POWERS

Advanced armoured suit gives super strength, flight and concussive blasts.

ORIGINS

Boris Bullski is a KGB member who created a nearly unbreakable suit of armour to fight Iron Man. Although he has been thoroughly beaten by Tony Stark several times, he keeps upgrading his suit and often works as a mercenary, selling his talents for destruction to the highest bidder. The Titanium Man suit is bigger and stronger than the Iron Man armour, and Bullski has taken treatments that have made him grow to superhuman size within the suit.

UNKNOWN
SPYMASTER

POWERS

Expert in espionage and sabotage.

ORIGINS

The fact that very little is known about the Spymaster's history shows how good he is at his job. The Spymaster is one of only a few people who have been able to steal the secrets of Tony Stark's Iron Man armour, selling them to Tony's rival Justin Hammer. He has fought Spider-Man and Iron Man many times, and is exceptionally good at espionage and infiltration, using spy devices such as razor-disks, jet boots and wrist-mounted blasters. Spymaster has little to no moral code and sells his secrets to the highest bidder.

The Spymaster killed Happy Hogan, Tony Stark's bodyguard and confidant.

ANTON VANKO
WHIPLASH

POWERS

Suit of armour with energy whips in the wrists.

ORIGINS

Several criminals have used the name Whiplash, but Anton Vanko has the deepest connection to Tony Stark. Vanko's father was killed by an impostor wearing Iron Man armour, and Vanko created a suit of armour with deadly energised whips in the wrists to get his revenge. Despite discovering that someone else killed his father, Vanko still blames Stark and wants him dead. Whiplash's electrically-charged whips are very dangerous and can cut through metal, including Iron Man's armour.

CHAPTER THREE
CAPTAIN AMERICA

NICK FURY'S NOTES

One of the hardest things you'll ever have to do as Director of S.H.I.E.L.D. is stand up to a living legend. Steve Rogers made sacrifices that allow this organisation to operate the way it does today, and he has returned time and time again whenever S.H.I.E.L.D. needs him most. When you stand next to him, you realise that you're standing next to a part of history.

Doesn't mean he's always right, though. Steve is a brilliant man, but he's from a different time, and I have to make difficult decisions when Captain America can't. And if I do my job right, he will never know about it.

STEVE ROGERS
CAPTAIN AMERICA

POWERS

Superhuman speed, strength, stamina, durability and athleticism. Master tactician.

Captain America has lead many teams of Avengers and is an inspiration for super heroes all over the world.

ORIGINS

Deemed unfit to join the army in World War II, brave but scrawny Steve Rogers volunteered to take the experimental Super-Soldier serum which transformed him into one of the world's mightiest heroes. At the end of the war he was lost, frozen in ice, but was revived years later by the Avengers. A man out of time, Captain America leads the Avengers with complete moral authority and the respect of his peers. Cap has a virtually indestructible Vibranium shield, super strength and a natural ability for tactics and strategy.

JAMES BUCHANAN 'BUCKY' BARNES
THE WINTER SOLDIER

POWERS

Advanced combat training and marksmanship. Powerful metal arm.

The Winter Soldier has a super strong bionic arm.

ORIGINS

Bucky Barnes was Captain America's best friend and sidekick during World War II, but he went missing and was presumed dead. In reality he had been captured and brainwashed by the evil Armin Zola, turning him into a legendary Soviet assassin called the Winter Soldier. Bucky operated as the Winter Soldier for decades before Steve Rogers was able to find him and help him remember his former life. Bucky is haunted by his time as an assassin, and tries to make amends for the horrific acts he has committed.

SAM WILSON
FALCON

POWERS

Flight suit. Trained in hand-to-hand combat. Can talk to birds.

ORIGINS

Aided by a flight harness that was designed by Black Panther, as well as the ability to talk to birds, Sam Wilson has been Captain America's friend and partner for many years. In addition to being an Avenger, Sam is a social worker in Harlem and he tries to use his career as a hero to spread peace and understanding. Sam has stepped up and taken on the role of Captain America during times when Steve Rogers can't, and has proved to be adept at wielding the iconic shield.

SHARON CARTER
AGENT 13

POWERS

Trained in martial arts, espionage and firearms.

ORIGINS

When your great-aunt is World War II legend Peggy Carter you have a lot to live up to. Sharon Carter has more than proved herself – she is a renowned S.H.I.E.L.D. agent, known for her work in taking down A.I.M. (Advanced Idea Mechanics), Hydra and the Red Skull. The romantic relationship between Sharon and Steve Rogers has been slightly complicated by his history with her great-aunt, but the two work brilliantly together and have a high success rate when it comes to protecting the world.

JOHAN SCHMIDT
RED SKULL

POWERS

Expert tactician, skilled marksman and hand-to-hand combatant.

ORIGINS

Captain America's nemesis was a high-ranking Nazi officer during World War II and he has resurfaced in the modern age. Part of the terrorist organisation Hydra, the Red Skull wants nothing less than to rule the world. Johan Schmidt is one of the most intelligent and most devious villains that Captain America has ever faced, and is constantly coming up with diabolical new schemes. The Red Skull's distinctive look was originally a mask, but after a disfiguring fight with Cap, the skull is his real face.

The Red Skull has placed his consciousness in different bodies over the years.

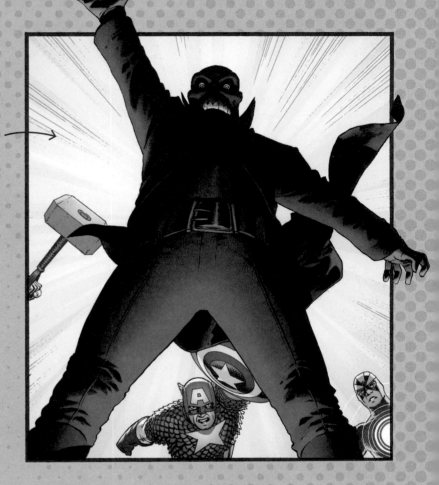

HEINRICH ZEMO AND HELMUT ZEMO
BARON ZEMO

POWERS

Hand-to-hand combat and marksmanship.

ORIGINS

During World War II Captain America fought Heinrich Zemo, a German weapons manufacturer. After their first encounter Baron Zemo's mask became permanently glued to his face, which was a source of much embarrassment to Zemo. Years later, Heinrich's son Helmut took on the mantle of Baron Zemo, and plotted to destroy Captain America. Helmut's mask is not glued to his face, but he wears it to hide scars that he sustained in a battle. The younger Baron Zemo is a shrewd tactical operator, and has controlled many heroes and villains without them knowing it.

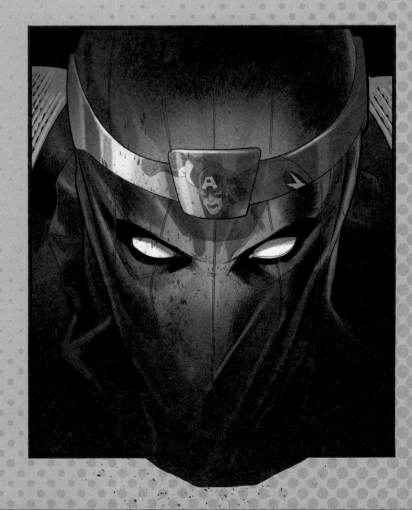

ARNIM ZOLA

ARNIM ZOLA

POWERS

Robot body gives mind control.

ORIGINS

Arnim Zola worked for the Red Skull during World War II, trying to use genetic engineering to create super soldiers for the Germans. After the war he managed to upload his brain into a robot body, granting himself a form of clunking digital immortality. Zemo's work in transferring consciousness is pioneering, and he has been able to save his own life by moving his mind across computer networks. Zola has allied himself with Hydra, and commands considerable Hydra forces. He can control his enemies' minds using a variety of different methods.

GEORGE TARLETON

M.O.D.O.K.

POWERS

Superhuman intelligence, psionic blasts, chair equipped with lasers and rockets.

M.O.D.O.K. may look bizarre but he is a scientific and criminal genius.

ORIGINS

A.I.M. technician George Tarleton was 'persuaded' to undergo a mutagenic process to become a living computer called M.O.D.O.C. (Mobile Organism Designed Only for Computing). Tarleton became something else, calling himself M.O.D.O.K. (Mobile Organism Designed Only for Killing), murdering his superiors and taking control of A.I.M. as Scientist Supreme. M.O.D.O.K.'s enhanced brain allows him telepathy, mind control and psionic blasts, but his giant head is too big for his body to support so he needs a hoverchair and exoskeleton to survive.

CHAPTER FOUR

THE HULK

NICK FURY'S NOTES

There aren't many things in the world that scare me, but, when I look into Doctor Banner's eyes, I get scared. I think he's used to that, which is why he keeps returning to people like Betty Ross, Jennifer Walters and Rick Jones who aren't scared of him.

The Hulk claims that all he wants to do is smash, but Banner has built up a fairly decent support network over the years. For a while he even started spending time with the Avengers, after shunning the team since being part of its foundation. Although the Hulk says he just wants to be left alone, he clearly doesn't.

DOCTOR ROBERT BRUCE BANNER
HULK

POWERS

Full level of strength may never have been measured.

ORIGINS

Doctor Bruce Banner ran to save teenager Rick Jones from a gamma explosion, throwing himself in the way of the blast. Forever altered by the radiation, he transforms into a being of pure strength and rage. The angrier the Hulk gets, the stronger the Hulk gets, and we still may not know the full limits of his strength or his rage. The Hulk is a founding member of the Avengers, but his natural inclination for solitude means that he does not join the team on many missions.

RICHARD MILHOUSE JONES
RICK JONES

POWERS

Combat training.

ORIGINS

Rick Jones is right at the centre of the super hero world. After Bruce Banner saved him from an atomic blast, Jones was the only one who knew about Banner's dual identity and he became close friends with the Hulk. Jones was later Captain America's sidekick, briefly taking the place of the original Bucky. Later he became linked to Mar-Vell, with the two swapping bodies using cosmic Nega-Bands. For a while Rick had the strength and powers of The Abomination, calling himself A-Bomb.

Rick seems to be a magnet for super heroes.

JENNIFER WALTERS
SHE-HULK

POWERS

Top-level strength and durability.

Unlike Bruce, Jen retains her intelligence when she transforms.

ORIGINS

Lawyer Jennifer Walters was seriously wounded, and the only way to save her life was a blood transfusion from her cousin Bruce Banner. The radioactive blood gave Jennifer new powers, and she became the She-Hulk. Jennifer can now control her transformations, and prefers to stay in her green form. She-Hulk is a valued member of the Avengers and even filled in for Ben Grimm as part of the Fantastic Four. Jennifer still practises law, and backs up her sensational strength with her razor-sharp wits.

BETTY ROSS
BETTY ROSS

POWERS

Varies.

ORIGINS

Being married to the Incredible Hulk isn't easy, and it's even harder when you are the daughter of General Thunderbolt Ross, the man tasked with taking the Hulk down. Betty's love for Bruce can be seen in some ways as a rebellion against her father, but Bruce and Betty genuinely care for each other. At different times Betty has been transformed into the rampaging Red She-Hulk and also the winged Harpy. She is strong-willed, intelligent and one of the few people in the world who the Hulk trusts

EMIL BLONSKY
ABOMINATION

POWERS

Super strength and durability.

ORIGINS

Like the Hulk, Emil Blonsky was transformed into a green-skinned monster by a huge dose of gamma radiation, but unlike the Hulk, Emil is unable to transform back to human form. Blonsky's metamorphosis into the grotesque Abomination alienated his wife Nadia, and the loss of his wife drove him insane. A former Soviet spy, Blonsky is bigger and possibly even stronger than the Hulk, and he has a deep personal hatred for Banner because he is convinced that Banner is the cause of all his problems.

GENERAL THADDEUS 'THUNDERBOLT' ROSS
RED HULK

POWERS

Top-level strength and durability.

Instead of getting stronger when he gets angry, the Red Hulk gets hotter.

ORIGINS

The father of Bruce Banner's wife Betty, General Thunderbolt Ross was in charge of hunting down the Hulk for years. Eventually General Ross became so frustrated with his inability to stop the Hulk that he bombarded himself with gamma radiation, turning himself into the Red Hulk. The Red Hulk has similar powers and strength to the original Hulk, but he gets hotter instead of stronger when he gets angry. Ross is tactically smarter than the Hulk, but doesn't have his experience, raw anger or heroism.

CARL 'CRUSHER' CREEL
ABSORBING MAN

POWERS

Can absorb and duplicate the properties of anything he touches.

ORIGINS

Petty criminal and prisoner Crusher Creel drank a magic potion taken from the Asgardian trickster god Loki, which gives him the ability to absorb the properties of anything he touches. Creel immediately gained power on a par with that of Thor and the Hulk, and began battling super heroes whenever they got in his way. The Absorbing Man wields the ball and chain that were used to shackle him as a prison inmate. Creel can absorb the properties of almost anything, from Adamantium to Thor's magic hammer.

The Absorbing Man is married to Titania, and the two often work as a team.

SAMUEL STERNS
THE LEADER

POWERS

Superhuman intelligence. Some psionic powers.

ORIGINS

Being hit by gamma radiation didn't give janitor Samuel Sterns super strength – it super-powered his mind instead. The Leader is fearsomely intelligent and has spent years trying to take over the world, striving to turn humanity into green-skinned reflections of himself. The Leader loves to build incredibly complex machines and robots, and is one of the world's experts in gamma radiation. In many ways the Leader is the opposite of the Hulk, his high level of intelligence contrasting with Banner's impossible strength.

CHAPTER FIVE
THOR AND ASGARD

NICK FURY'S NOTES

The lives and loves of Viking space gods should be a bit above my pay grade, but when their battles start spilling out onto Earth then I have to start getting involved. Normally I can rely on Thor to clean up his own messes, but sometimes things can get a bit hot, and that's when it pays to know every actor involved.

As far as I can tell, Thor's father Odin is a slippery customer. He seems to like being a few steps ahead of everyone else with a few tricks up his sleeve. I can appreciate that sort of thinking.

THOR ODINSON
THOR

POWERS

Super strength and durability. Controls the weather. Magic hammer.

Thor is destined to lead Asgard.

ORIGINS

The Norse god of thunder splits his time between helping the Avengers on Earth and serving his people in the realm of Asgard. Thor uses the mystical hammer Mjolnir, which can only be wielded by those who are worthy. He is hundreds of years old, and much to his father Odin's annoyance, has been travelling to Earth since the time of the Vikings. Thor is a seasoned warrior, though his brashness and love of battle can often get him into trouble, especially when it comes to more delicate Avengers missions.

JANE FOSTER
VALKYRIE

POWERS

Super strength and durability. Flight. Shape-shifting weapon.

ORIGINS

Doctor Jane Foster was in love with Thor Odinson, but a relationship between a human and Asgardian proved too difficult and they separated. Years later, Jane was diagnosed with breast cancer, and shortly after picked up Mjolnir, transforming her into Thor, the Goddess of Thunder. At the time Thor Odinson was unworthy of the hammer, so as the goddess of thunder, Jane joined the Avengers. Jane has since been cured of cancer and is now the first of a new generation of Valkyries, protecting Asgard and Earth.

ODIN BORSON

ODIN

POWERS

The Odin Force gives Odin a wide range of magic powers.

Odin is a wily and cunning manipulator, just like his stepson Loki.

ORIGINS

Odin was a warrior in his youth. Around 1,000,000 BC he formed a prototype version of the Avengers with early versions of Black Panther, the Phoenix and other heroes. Odin is a veteran of many Norse wars. Centuries ago he and his brothers fought Surtur the fire demon, but only Odin survived. The mother of Odin's son Thor is the Earth goddess Gaea, but Thor was raised by the Asgardian Freyja. Odin has one eye because he sacrificed his right eye for the wisdom to stop Ragnarok, and he uses this wisdom to rule Asgard.

FRIGGA FREYRDOTTIR

FRIGGA

POWERS

Access to a wide range of Norse magic.

ORIGINS

The Queen of Asgard and Thor's stepmother, Frigga uses magic to keep her Asgardian subjects safe from harm. Frigga's father, Freyr, fought Odin for years until a truce was struck where Frigga and Odin were married to keep the peace. Frigga is the Asgardian goddess of marriage and the All-Mother, and she rules Asgard when Odin is recuperating in his Odinsleep. She is no stranger to palace intrigue as she has to stay one step ahead of her adoptive son, Loki.

LOKI LAUFEYSON
LOKI

POWERS

Illusions, shapeshifting, telepathy.

ORIGINS

Loki is the Asgardian god of mischief, and he uses his magic powers of illusion to create chaos wherever he goes. The son of Laufey the frost giant, Loki was adopted by Odin. Loki always resented his brother Thor, and the two have spent years battling each other. Sometimes mischievous, sometimes evil, Loki is a complicated and difficult villain. Loki is directly responsible for the formation of the Avengers, after he framed the Hulk for a crime he did not commit – the Earth's mightiest heroes teamed up to clear his name.

Do not trust a single thing that Loki says!

HELA
HELA

POWERS

Commands the dead. High-level magic user.

ORIGINS

If an Asgardian dies an honoured death then the Valkyries take their soul to Valhalla. If they don't die an honoured death, they go to Hel or Niflheim. These two realms are ruled over by Hela, the Goddess of Death. Hela has ambitions to conquer Valhalla and Asgard (and all the other realms), but she has always been held back by Odin and Thor. Hela has an army of the dead at her command, and is so powerful that she can kill or resurrect mortals merely by touching them.

SURTUR

POWERS

Fire demon. Magic use. Fire manipulation.

ORIGINS

Surtur is a fire demon from the realm of Muspelheim, and his main objectives are destruction, flames and murder of all of the Ten Realms. After a pitch battle Odin imprisoned Surtur for centuries, but Loki later freed Surtur to cause havoc on Earth. Surtur is huge, standing over 1,000 feet tall when at full power. He is able to change shape and rain fire on his enemies, and he equals Odin in sheer magical power.

Surtur is destined to be part of Ragnarok, the legendary end of Asgard.

MALEKITH THE ACCURSED

POWERS

Superhuman strength and reflexes. Dark magic user. Controls the Wild Hunt.

ORIGINS

The Asgardian realm of Svartalfheim is home to Dark Elves who are ruled by the vicious and arrogant Malekith the Accursed. Malekith was captured by trolls as a child, and trained in magic by a fellow captive who was a wizard. Unable to control his vicious nature, Malekith killed the wizard, but half his face was burned in the battle. One of Malekith's magical abilities is to summon the Wild Hunt, a pack of wild dogs that he uses to track his enemies.

VILLAINS

51

SIF

SIF

POWERS

Exceptional swordfighter, superhuman strength and endurance.

ORIGINS

Thor's childhood companion is one of the fiercest warriors in Asgard, and defends the realm from all threats. Although Thor's affections lie elsewhere, Sif has long harboured romantic feelings for the god of thunder. Sif is the sister of Heimdall, and often battles beside Balder and the Warriors Three. Like all of Thor's companions, Sif has had many run-ins with Loki – Sif's hair was originally golden, but in a fit of jealousy over her bravery in battle, Loki cut her hair and replaced it with hair made by dwarves.

VOLSTAGG, HOGUN THE GRIM AND FANDRAL THE DASHING

THE WARRIORS THREE

POWERS

Superhuman strength and stamina.

Volstagg once took Thor's place as the War Thor.

ORIGINS

Volstagg, Hogun and Fandral make up the Warriors Three, Thor's greatest friends and battle companions. Volstagg is the largest of the Warriors Three – a brave fighter who has a large family with an unspecified number of children. Hogun is the quietest of the group, and is known for his taciturn manner. Fandral the Dashing is a swashbuckler and considers himself quite the ladies' man. Thor knows that he can count on the Warriors Three for any adventure.

HERCULES

POWERS

Superhuman strength, endurance and agility.
Skilled in archery and combat.

ORIGINS

Although Hercules is not from Asgard, the Olympian demigod is a firm friend and ally of Thor. Both gods share a love of adventure, battle and revelry. Thor and Hercules have fought each other more than once, but trust each other completely. Hercules is a longstanding member of the Avengers, and has upper-level power limits given to him by his father Zeus. He is so strong that he can fight Thor or the Hulk and bring them to a standstill.

The Olympian Gods can be accessed through a special route on Mount Olympus.

ALDRIF ODINSDOTTIR
ANGELA

POWERS

Superhuman strength, endurance and agility. Flight.

ORIGINS

For years Thor and Loki had no idea that they had a sister. Angela was born Aldrif, the daughter of Odin and Freyja, who was thought to have been killed in Asgard's war with the Tenth Realm, Heaven. Unknown to Odin, Angela was then raised by angels, away from the view of Asgard, because the link between the realms was severed. Angela has Asgardian-level strength, and was trained in combat by warrior angels. She is naturally distrustful of her real family, having been raised by angels to see Asgardians as the enemy.

ULIK

POWERS

Superhuman strength and stamina.

ORIGINS

A Rock Troll from the realm of Nornheim, Ulik first followed orders from Geirrodur, the King of the Rock Trolls, who hates Asgardians because years ago they forced the Trolls to live underground. Other enemies may be smart and devious, but Ulik is just one tough Troll. Ulik seems to grow in strength during battles, and by the end of a fight he is stronger than Thor. These days Ulik rules his own kingdom of violent Rock Trolls.

Ulik is much, much more poweful than other Rock Trolls.

AMORA

ENCHANTRESS

POWERS

Superhuman strength. Magic powers including illusions and telepathy.

ORIGINS

Amora is one of the most powerful magic users in Asgard, which makes her one of the most powerful beings in the universe. She was part of Odin's court at Asgard before being banished to Earth for defying Odin. The Enchantress is extremely beautiful, and has been romantically involved with Thor in the past. She is unencumbered by human morality, and is motivated mainly by self interest, using her spells to control and enslave anyone who she thinks will help her. The Enchantress has joined several super villain teams including Baron Zemo's Masters of Evil.

SKURGE
EXECUTIONER

POWERS

Superhuman strength, endurance and agility. Skilled in archery and combat.

ORIGINS

Enchantress loves to manipulate people, and there is no-one who she has manipulated as often (or as willingly) as Skurge. Once a brave Asgardian who fought Storm giants, Skurge was enticed into fighting Thor by Amora and has been battling super heroes ever since. Both Loki and the Enchantress have used Skurge as part of their evil plans. Odin banished Skurge to Earth at the same time as the Enchantress, and Skurge has enjoyed causing trouble on Midgard. Though he is trained in Asgardian weapons, Skurge also appreciates weapons from Earth.

Skurge is quite a fan of semi-automatic rifles.

GORR
GORR, THE GOD BUTCHER

POWERS

Superhuman strength and stamina. Necrosword.

Gorr has killed different dieties from all over the universe.

ORIGINS

Gorr spent centuries tracking and killing gods from hundreds of different pantheons. He hates all gods because he blames them for the death of his family. Gorr's weapon is All-Black, the Necrosword, which is similar to Venom's symbiote costume as it was created by Knull, the King of the Symbiotes. As well as allowing Gorr to fly and travel in space, the Necrosword can create a small army of Berserkers which are strong enough to strike down most of his opponents. Gorr was eventually killed by three time-travelling Thors, but not before he killed many, many gods.

HEIMDALL

POWERS

Superhuman strength and stamina. Teleportation. Can see and hear thoughout the Ten Realms.

ORIGINS

The rainbow bridge Bifrost needs a stern and attentive sentry, and Heimdall takes his responsibilities very seriously. The brother of the warrior Sif, Heimdall is himself well-trained in the art of battle. Every attack on Asgard has to go through Heimdall, and he has fought a wide range of intruders, including trolls, giants, dwarves and even super heroes. Heimdall's vision and hearing have to be incredibly powerful, as he is always listening out for attacks on Asgard. The realm of Asgard has moved around a lot, but it has always had Heimdall to defend it.

BETA RAY BILL

POWERS

Superhuman strength and stamina. Enchanted hammer.

Beta Ray Bill has been a member of the Guardians of the Galaxy and Omega Flight.

ORIGINS

The hammer Mjolnir is enchanted so that anyone who is worthy can pick it up, even if they are an alien from another galaxy. A Korbinite who was enhanced with the DNA of the Korbinite's greatest predator, Bill is from a galaxy destroyed by Surtur. He led his people to our galaxy, where he was confronted by Thor. During the resulting battle Bill picked up Thor's hammer and gained the power of Thor. Seeing that Beta Ray Bill was worthy, Odin fashioned him his own hammer out of magic Uru metal called Stormbreaker, and Bill and Thor are now close allies.

BALDER

BALDER THE BRAVE

POWERS

Superhuman strength and stamina. Light generation.

ORIGINS

Thor's brother is one of the bravest and most beloved warriors in Asgard. The Norse prophecy states that Balder's death will mean the start of Ragnarok and the end of Asgard. Many spells have been cast on Balder in an attempt to stop Ragnarok, making him invulnerable to everything except mistletoe when he is on Asgard. As a Prince of Asgard, Balder often assumes responsibility for the realm, but has been easily manipulated by his adopted brother Loki many times. Balder is the Asgardian god of light, and can generate beams of intense light and heat.

ERIC MASTERSON

THUNDERSTRIKE

POWERS

Magic hammer gives super strength, flight and energy blasts.

Thunderstrike's mace is not quite as powerful as Thor's hammer, Mjolnir.

ORIGINS

There are only a handful of mortals who have proved worthy of the power of Thor. Eric filled in for Thor while Odinson was missing, taking his place as an Avenger. Eric was Thor during the climactic events of the Infinity Gauntlet saga. When Thor was finally found, Odin gave Eric an enchanted mace, and Eric then created his own super hero identity. The mace gave Thunderstrike similar, but slightly lesser powers to Thor. Eric died in battle, and years later his son Kevin Masterson took up the name of Thunderstrike.

57

CHAPTER SIX

HAWKEYE,
BLACK WIDOW
AND THE AVENGERS

NICK FURY'S NOTES

The Avengers is a big, crazy project that never should've worked. All of those big egos pushed together - something should've snapped years ago. There are too many big personalities for this to work.

And yet it works! I hate the fact that I don't have any real control of the Avengers and I'm worried that the whole thing is a disaster waiting to happen, but somehow they've managed to save the world time and time again. I've heard that some aliens don't call this planet Earth any more, they call it Avengers' World.

CLINTON 'CLINT' BARTON
HAWKEYE

POWERS

Top-level marksman. Exceptional at fencing and hand-to-hand combat.

ORIGINS

As a boy Clint Barton ran away to join the circus, where he was trained to become a master archer and fighter by Trick Shot and the Swordsman. Though Clint fought Iron Man the first time they met, Hawkeye is now a key member of the Avengers. Hawkeye is amazingly accurate with projectiles and claims that he can turn any object into a weapon. Though Clint is an exceptional super hero he struggles to control his personal life, finding long-term relationships difficult to maintain.

Clint Barton has been training Kate Bishop, and both use the codename Hawkeye.

NATASHA ROMANOFF
BLACK WIDOW

POWERS

Skilled in espionage, weapons, hand-to-hand combat.

Natasha was subjected to procedures that increased her strength and lifespan.

ORIGINS

Despite her past as a Soviet spy, Natasha has proved that she is indispensable to both S.H.I.E.L.D. and the Avengers. Black Widow was trained in the Red Room Academy, where young women were turned into secret agents and deadly assassins. Natasha is not the only agent to use the Black Widow name, and was part of the deadly Black Widow ops programme. Black Widow is able to make the hard choices that other heroes won't, and will do whatever is necessary to complete the mission.

HANK PYM AND SCOTT LANG
ANT-MAN

POWERS

Can change size to a subatomic level.

ORIGINS

Hank Pym, the first Ant-Man, developed Pym Particles which could change a subject's size and mass in seconds. Hank was a founding member of the Avengers, and also used his particles to grow in size, calling himself Goliath. Years later Scott Lang, a scientist and (semi) reformed criminal stole the Ant-Man suit so that he could rescue a doctor to help his daughter. Seeing potential on him, Hank passed on the mantle of Ant-Man to Scott who has added his own upgrades to the suit since.

Eric O'Grady also used the Ant-Man name, but he has since died.

JANET VAN DYNE
WASP

POWERS

Can change size, subdermal wings allow flight.

ORIGINS

Hank Pym fell in love with his business partner's daughter, and gave her a super hero outfit, subdermal wings and the ability to shrink using Pym Particles. Janet Van Dyne is an original member of the Avengers, and was the one who came up with the name for the team. As well as being a fearless super hero she is also a talented fashion designer and has created many super hero costumes. Hank Pym's daughter from his first marriage, Nadia van Dyne, has recently become the Wasp with Janet's blessing.

ALEXEI SHOSTAKOV
RED GUARDIAN

POWERS

Advanced combat training.

There have been at least seven Red Guardians that we know of. →

ORIGINS

Ever since Captain America first led the charge in World War II, pretty much every other country has wanted their own super soldier. The first Red Guardian was a soldier during World War II, but the super hero identity was passed on to other operatives.

Alexei Shostakov, the husband of Natasha Romanoff, was the Red Guardian, often battling US agents and heroes. Shostakov died saving Black Widow and Captain America, and several other super humans have worn the Red Guardian costume since.

JACQUES DUQUESNE
SWORDSMAN

POWERS

Top-level bladed combat and marksmanship.

ORIGINS

The Swordsman was a master of all bladed weapons and wielded a specially modified sword which could fire blasts of varying strength and lethality. He has been both a villain and a hero – he has been a member of both the Lethal Legion and the Avengers. When he became a member of the Avengers he joined his former protégé Hawkeye, but Clint Barton was distrustful of his motives. Duquesne died on an Avengers mission, killed by inter-temporal warlord Kang. Despite dying a hero, Duquesne has created a villainous legacy for himself, and the Swordsman costume has been picked up by several other super villains since.

ULTRON
ULTRON

POWERS

Genius-level intelligence, flight, energy blasts, can project consciousness.

ORIGINS

Ultron is Hank Pym's greatest regret. Pym was trying to create artificial intelligence and placed a programme based on his own brain patterns in a robot body. Ultron gained sentience, became independent and rebelled against his creator, and is now a world-class Avengers foe. Ultron is fearsomely intelligent, incredibly strong and devious enough to enjoy manipulating his enemies. Ultron can move between Adamantium-hard robot bodies and control hundreds at the same time. He can also project his consciousness into different machines.

Ultron is a world-level threat.

UNKNOWN
TASKMASTER

POWERS

Can copy anyone's fight patterns after seeing them once.

ORIGINS

Taskmaster has photographic reflexes, which means that he can replicate any physical action that he sees, even if only once in a video. He used his abilities to become a super criminal, copying moves from super heroes to pull off dangerous robberies, then fighting any heroes who tried to stop him. Taskmaster has worked for S.H.I.E.L.D. but generally his loyalties belong to whoever will pay him the most money. He carries replicas of Captain America's shield and Hawkeye's arrows, believing himself to be the equal of any Avenger.

VILLAINS

T'CHALLA
BLACK PANTHER

POWERS

Superhuman strength. Advanced Wakandan technology. Talks to the dead.

Wakandan technology is both incredibly advanced and always improving. T'Challa should not be underestimated.

ORIGINS

The Black Panther is the protector and ruler of the hidden African nation of Wakanda. T'Challa became the Black Panther after his father T'Chaka died – after drinking special herbs T'Challa was given super human strength, speed and agility, and the ability to draw on the experiences of previous Black Panthers. T'Challa's costume is made from unbreakable Vibranium and is augmented by Wakandan equipment that is far in advance of our own. Black Panther is an irregular member of the Avengers, since he provides both incredible strength and intellect.

SHURI
SHURI

POWERS

Super intelligence, strength, speed and agility. Can temporarily reanimate Wakandan dead. Supernatural powers including ability to transform into flock of birds.

ORIGINS

T'Challa's sister Shuri is the princess of Wakanda and a scientific genius. Shuri took on the role of Black Panther while T'Challa was unable, proving herself to be a brave super hero and a wise Chief of Wakanda. Only the strongest and bravest can complete the trials to become a Black Panther, and when she completed them Shuri was granted super strength, agility and speed. Shuri is a brilliant inventor, taking the already advanced Wakandan technology further than ever seen before.

DANE WHITMAN
BLACK KNIGHT

POWERS

Exceptional swordsman. Magic sword and flying horse.

ORIGINS

The Black Knight title has been passed down through generations since the court of King Arthur in Medieval England. American Dane Whitman became the Black Knight after his uncle, who has been a villainous Black Knight, begged him to restore honour to the family name. Dane wielded the Ebony Blade – a cursed magical weapon that could cut through almost anything and make its user invulnerable. Riding his white winged horse called Aragorn, the Black Knight was a brave and courageous Avenger.

BRIAN BRADDOCK, BETSY BRADDOCK
CAPTAIN BRITAIN

POWERS

Superhuman strength, speed and reflexes. Flight. Energy blasts.

Captain Britain's powers are both magical and techological.

ORIGINS

Brian Braddock is Britain's greatest super hero, using his super powers to protect the universe and inspire the country he loves. Transformed into Captain Britain by King Arthur's wizard Merlyn, Brian has magical powers which he regulates with the help of his technologically-advanced battlesuit. Captain Britain is a legendary presence in the UK, and he was the leader of the super hero teams Excalibur, the Knights of Pendragon and MI:13. Brian is the twin of Betsy Braddock, forrmerly Psylocke from the X-Men, who later took his role as Captain Britian.

ULYSSES KLAUE
KLAW

POWERS

Energy blasts.
Can create 'solid sound' constructs.

Klaw can create hard light constructs to defend himself or attack his enemies.

ORIGINS

Ulysses Klaue travelled to Wakanda to steal their legendary metal Vibranium, and when T'Challa's father T'Chaka tried to stop him, Klaue killed T'Chaka. Klaue lost his right hand in the battle and later had it replaced with a sonic emitter. Now calling himself Klaw, he could transform himself into a being of pure sound, as well as creating weapons out of sound. Klaw is a particularly vicious and unrepentant criminal, and has repeatedly targeted Black Panther and Wakanda. Years of turning his body into sound have done something awful to Klaw's mind, and he is extremely unstable.

N'JADAKA
ERIK KILLMONGER

POWERS

Martial arts training.

ORIGINS

Killmonger was born in Wakanda, and was known as N'Jadaka, son of N'Jobu. Ulysses Klaue forced N'Jobu to fight against T'Chaka, and N'Jobu's family were exiled from Wakanda when he lost the battle. N'Jadaka relocated to Harlem, New York, where he changed his name to Erik Killmonger. He then trained hard to become Black Panther's equal. Killmonger has returned to Wakanda several times, challenging T'Challa for the rulership and direction of Wakanda. Killmonger has incredible martial arts training and has previously beaten Black Panther in unarmed combat.

LUCHINO NEFARIA
COUNT NEFARIA

POWERS

Flight. Energy manipulation. Superhuman strength, speed, stamina.

ORIGINS

A greedy Italian nobleman, Count Nefaria became a leading figure in the Maggia crime cartel. When the Avengers tried to stop his criminal activities he attempted to frame them for treason but was foiled and humiliated. Ostracised from the Maggia, he used a group of super villains to give him super powers, becoming a powerful master of ionic energy. Though the Avengers have defeated him in the past, he is capable of overwhelming them in terms of sheer power. Nefaria believes that he should rule the world, and is a criminal mastermind.

NATHANIEL RICHARDS AKA IMMORTUS AKA IRON LAD AKA RAMA TUT AKA SCARLET CENTURION
KANG THE CONQUEROR

POWERS

Time travel technology, genius intellect.

Due to his journeys in the time stream, there are different versions of Kang, each with different histories and motivations.

ORIGINS

It's hard to pin down Kang's history exactly because he has moved through time so much. Nathaniel Richards was born around the year 3000, and discovering his ancestor Reed Richard's time machine he travelled back to ancient Egypt where he ruled as Pharoah Rama-Tut. After fighting time-travelling heroes he became Kang the Conqueror, subjugating the 40th century, then returning to fight the Avengers repeatedly in the present day. Alternate versions of Kang exist, where he was a young hero called Iron Lad and an old man called Immortus.

67

WANDA MAXIMOFF
SCARLET WITCH

POWERS

Hex powers allow her to control Chaos Magic.

ORIGINS

Wanda grew up thinking she was the daughter of X-Men villain Magneto, but after much soul searching Wanda and her brother Quicksilver left the Brotherhood of Evil Mutants to become heroes and join the Avengers. The Scarlet Witch has top-level powers and has been trained to use Chaos Magic to manipulate energy and matter. Wanda has struggled with her awesome powers – she completely rewrote reality when she suffered a mental breakdown, but she works hard every day to control herself.

Wanda's Chaos Magic can alter the nature of the universe. She is perhaps the most powerful Avenger.

PIETRO MAXIMOFF
QUICKSILVER

POWERS

Super speed.

ORIGINS

Pietro is a super hero who can move at supersonic speeds – he can sometimes seem a little arrogant to other heroes because everyone else in the world is slow and sluggish to him. Quicksilver and the Scarlet Witch became Avengers after the initial line up left, and even though there was a little trepidation about two former villains joining the team, they both proved excellent recruits. For years Pietro and Wanda thought that Magneto was their father, but their real father is the High Evolutionary.

VISION

VISION

POWERS

Can control own density, superhuman strength and speed.

The Vision created an artificial family to try to understand what it is like to be human. His daughter, Viv, is also a hero. →

ORIGINS

The Vision is an artificial intelligence, a synthezoid, created by Ultron to attack the Avengers. Vision was able to break free of his programming and help the Avengers, and shortly after he joined the team as a valued member. Vision and the Scarlet Witch fell in love and were married, but the marriage has since dissolved. As a synthetic being, Vision is able to alter the density of his own body which means he can alternate between being so light that he can walk through walls and being so heavy that he can crush concrete.

ROBERT REYNOLDS

THE SENTRY

POWERS

Superhuman strength, speed, stamina. Invulnerability.

ORIGINS

Though he was a super hero for years, nobody could remember The Sentry – not even himself. Robert Reynolds took a special serum that gave him incredible powers, but also unleashed his dark side. His dark side became a dangerous super villain called the Void. To save the world from the Void, the Sentry erased himself from the minds of everyone on Earth, including his own. The Sentry did reappear, and is closely monitored by the Avengers in case the Void returns.

Bob Reynolds is a psychologically unwell man with the powers of a god. He should be monitored VERY closely.

DIRK GARTHWAITE, HENRY CAMP, DR ELIOT FRANKLIN AND BRIAN CALUSKY

WRECKING CREW

POWERS

Superhuman strength and magic weapons.

ORIGINS

The Wrecking Crew are a hardened team of career criminals who gained magic Asgardian powers and use them to go on destructive crime sprees. The leader, the Wrecker, wields an enchanted crowbar, and he is backed up by Bulldozer, Piledriver and Thunderball. Though the Wrecking Crew are some of the strongest criminals that the Avengers have ever fought, they are not very effective and seem to spend most of their time in prison.

GEORGE BATROC

BATROC THE LEAPER

POWERS

Hand-to-hand combat training.
Top-level human agility. Kickboxing.

ORIGINS

A French national, Batroc is one of the world's greatest kickboxers and is able to leap incredible distances. Although he is a deadly mercenary, Batroc has a strict code of honour and will not fight for anyone who he feels is dishonourable. He has primarily fought Captain America, but was part of a force that tried to invade Wakanda. Batroc occasionally leads a team called Batroc's Brigade, but they are not always very successful.

For a man whose main power is jumping, Batroc has been incredibly successful.

HEBERT EDGAR WYNDHAM
HIGH EVOLUTIONARY

POWERS

Superhuman intelligence. Matter and energy manipulation.

The High Evolutionary used his knowledge of genetics to create new races to guard Mount Wundagore.

ORIGINS

The imposing High Evolutionary was once a student from Manchester called Hebert Wyndham who managed to crack the human genetic code. Wyndham isolated himself in Mount Wundagore, trying to create new forms of life called New Men. After battling the Avengers he left Earth, creating a replica of Earth on the other side of the Sun called Counter Earth. The High Evolutionary is as intelligent as it is possible for a human to be, and has altered his own genetic structure to give himself god-like powers.

MORGAN LE FAY
MORGAN LE FAY

POWERS

Magic. Immortality.

ORIGINS

A foe of the legendary King Arthur, Morgan le Fay is a half-faerie magic user who has used her spells to interfere with the modern age. In the sixth century she was visited by a time-travelling Doctor Doom who became her lover, but their evil plans were foiled by Iron Man. Le Fay then started using her spells to project herself into the present day, using her access to different dimensions to try to take over the world until she was stopped by the Avengers.

MONICA RAMBEAU
SPECTRUM

POWERS

Energy manipulation. Flight.
Can covert body to energy.

ORIGINS

New Orleans harbour patrol lieutenant Monica Rambeau was exposed to a strange, extra-dimensional energy which allowed her to change her body into pure energy. Calling herself Captain Marvel she became an outstanding super hero and eventually became leader of the Avengers. Her awesome energy-based powers and leadership abilities have allowed her to lead super hero teams both on and off planet. Monica has gone by many super hero names including Photon and Pulse, and she currently goes by the name of Spectrum.

MAR-VELL
MAR-VELL

POWERS

Superhuman strength, speed and endurance. Flight. Energy projection and absorption.

ORIGINS

The first Captain Marvel was a Kree soldier who came to investigate Earth and ended up staying. Mar-Vell was an inspirational super hero who fought hard for his adoptive planet and was a respected member of the super hero community. Even though he protected the Earth and the universe from galactic threats (including Thanos), he was seen as a traitor by the Kree. After years of adventuring Mar-Vell died from cancer, and was mourned by friend and foe alike.

Mar-Vell left the Kree Empire to protect the Earth.

CAROL DANVERS
CAPTAIN MARVEL

POWERS

Top-level strength, stamina and speed. Flight. Energy projection and absorption.

ORIGINS

Carol Danvers was a friend of the original Captain Marvel, and she has recently taken the name as a way of honouring the legacy of Mar-Vell. An Air Force officer, Carol gained her powers when she was caught in the explosion of a Kree device called a Pysche-Magnetron, making her a Kree-human hybrid. When at home Captain Marvel is one of the Avengers' heaviest hitters, but she prefers to patrol the galaxy, looking for the next threat to intergalactic peace.

Captain Marvel leads Alpha Flight, the Earth's defense force from hostile extraterrestrials. →

GENIS-VELL
GENIS-VELL

POWERS

Superhuman strength, speed and endurance. Flight.

ORIGINS

Genis-Vell is Mar-Vell's son, but he was born long after his father's death, created using Kree technology from his father's genetic material. Genis-Vell called himself Captain Marvel and took his father's Nega-Bands to give himself power. Rick Jones and Captain Marvel became linked using the Nega-Bands, taking turns to swap places in the negative zone. After he was separated from Rick Jones, Genis-Vell joined Baron Zemo's Thunderbolts and was killed by Zemo when he saw that Genis-Vell would destroy the universe.

MICHAEL KORVAC
KORVAC

POWERS

Cosmic powers.

Korvac's power is on a cosmic level.

ORIGINS

Born in an alternate universe in the year 2977, Michael Korvac travelled back to the present day, where he managed to steal the Power Cosmic from the worldship of Galactus. He is unstable and capricious, and he tried to reshape the Earth to his will, but was stopped by the Avengers and the Guardians of the Galaxy. Korvac then moved to the Forest Hills area of New York, where he lived happily and fell in love with Carina, the daughter of the Collector. Korvac was tracked down by the Avengers, and died after a pitch battle with the Earth's mightiest heroes.

BROCK RUMLOW
CROSSBONES

POWERS

Master of hand-to-hand combat and military weapons.

ORIGINS

Some people just seem to be born to fight, and Crossbones is one of them. Brock Rumlow was a cocky gang member in this youth, but he is now a hardened mercenary and one of the Red Skull's deadliest henchmen. Crossbones has a deep, personal hatred for Captain America, and has tried to assassinate him on more than one occasion. He is a master combatant, and keeps spring-loaded knives in his military gauntlets. Crossbones has no conscience and will happily kill without feeling any remorse.

UNKNOWN
BEYONDER

POWERS

Near omnipotence.

ORIGINS

There is a lot we don't know about the Beyonder. We know that he is a cosmic entity, a multi-dimensional being who may or may not be the most powerful presence in the universe. He once created a Battleworld, an interdimensional place where he forced heroes and villains to fight each other, which was the source of Spider-Man's black costume. The Beyonder can take human form, but he seems to be something the comes from beyond our comprehension of normal dimensions.

PARKER ROBBINS
THE HOOD

POWERS

Superhuman strength, speed and endurance. Flight.

The Hood's power also comes from his ability to unite the criminal underworld.

ORIGINS

It's always dangerous to see a street criminal with far more power than he knows how to handle. A chance encounter with a demon gave Parker Robbins boots of levitation and a cloak of invisibility, which he used to work his way up the super villain underworld. At first he was only trying to provide for his family, but soon he was corrupted by power and started referring to himself as The Hood. Although his plans have consistently been thwarted by super heroes, The Hood will always escalate his plans - he once collected all six Infinity Stones in an ill-fated attempt to battle the Avengers.

CHAPTER SEVEN
THE X-MEN

NICK FURY'S NOTES

Magneto is so angry because he thinks that the rest of the world have let the mutants down. He's probably right. Mutants have been attacked, persecuted and killed for years by a world that hates and fears them, even when the X-Men have been doing their best to save everybody.

Charles Xavier has recently created a new home for mutants on the Island of Krakoa, and I can't say that I blame him. I just wish there was another way.

CHARLES XAVIER
PROFESSOR X

POWERS

Omega-level psychic.

ORIGINS

Charles Xavier has always worked towards the dream that humans and mutants can live in peace. Deciding that mutants needed somewhere to learn about their abilities, Xavier founded the Xavier Institute, a safe haven for mutants and the home of the mutant super hero team the X-Men. Professor X is himself an immensely powerful mutant; he can manipulate minds, move objects with his mind and uses his Cerebro helmet to track, locate and record the minds of all mutants. He is an ambassador for mutankind, and has helped create a new home for them in the Island of Krakoa.

Charles Xavier now uses a portable Cerebro unit.

SCOTT SUMMERS
CYCLOPS

POWERS

Optic blasts.

Scott Summers lives with his family on the moon.

ORIGINS

One of the first class of X-Men, Scott Summers has always been seen as the de facto leader of the X-Men and has placed himself under a huge amount of pressure accordingly. Scott's first love was Jean Grey, but he later began a relationship with Emma Frost. Cyclops cannot control his mutant power of optic blasts naturally, so he wears a special visor (or sometimes ruby quartz glasses) to stop him from blasting everything he views. Though the blasts are powerful, his real power comes from his abilities a leader and master tactician.

JEAN GREY

JEAN GREY

POWERS

Telekinesis, telepathy.

The Phoenix Force has taken over other heroes, and has been split between X-Men.

ORIGINS

Thought she was the first mutant to enroll at Professor Xavier's school, Jean Grey's true potential was not obvious at first. Jean joined the X-Men under the code name Marvel Girl, and was a key member of the team. On a mission in space Jean was taken over by the the Phoenix Force, a powerful intergalactic entity that gave her nearly limitless psionic powers. Calling herself Phoenix, Jean was slowly corrupted by the power, and after she destroyed a whole planetary system she killed herself rather than do more damage. Jean has since returned and is no longer controlled by the Phoenix Force.

ROBERT 'BOBBY' DRAKE

ICEMAN

POWERS

Controls ice and temperature of the moisture in the air.

ORIGINS

Bobby Drake was the youngest of the original class of X-Men and always felt that he wasn't as respected as his classmates. Iceman's powers have evolved as he has trained with the X-Men – at first he used the water vapour in the air to create snowballs, but later he learned to freeze the water vapour in the air. As his training progressed he learned to create ice bridges, armour and projectiles. After being possessed by Emma Frost, he can now turn his body into organic ice, which he can form into powerful shapes.

MAX EISENHARDT AKA ERIK LEHNSHERR
MAGNETO

POWERS

Manipulation of magnetic fields.

Magneto uses his control of Earth's magnetic fields to allow himself to fly.

ORIGINS

Magneto believes that mutants are a superior species and must be forcibly protected from a world that fears and hates them. Mutants around the world have flocked to Magneto's cause, forming a Brotherhood of Mutants, who have clashed regularly with the X-Men. Magneto can manipulate magnetic fields, allowing him to fly, and he wears a helmet that protects his thoughts from his psychic former-friend, Charles Xavier. Magneto has joined the X-Men several times, fighting alongside his former foes when he thinks it is in the best interest of the mutant race. Magneto and Professor X have joined forces to find a new home for mutants on Krakoa.

RAVEN DARKHOLME
MYSTIQUE

POWERS

Shapeshifter.

ORIGINS

The most dangerous secret agent is one that you are convinced is someone else, and Mystique's mutant power allows her to look like anyone she wants. Mystique is so mysterious that her exact origin story isn't known. Her shape-shifting power means that she has no outward signs of aging, but she is estimated to be over a hundred years old. A key member of Magneto's Brotherhood of Mutants, Mystique has also occasionally joined the X-Men as part of various short-lived deals. Raven is the mother of Nightcrawler and the foster mother of Rogue, and has battled both in her clashes with the X-Men.

EN SABAH NUR
APOCALYPSE

POWERS

Molecular manipulation to give a wide range of super powers.

Apocalypse can control every aspect of his body. →

ORIGINS

One of the first mutants the world had ever seen, Apocalypse was born En Sabar Nur in Jordan thousands of years ago. After battling Pharaohs in Ancient Egypt he realised that his mutant power meant that he could not die, and Apocalypse began to think of himself as a god. Apocalypse believes in the absolute survival of the fittest, and that mankind must die for mutantkind to truly flourish. He spent several centuries in suspended animation, only to awaken in the modern age and try to create a new world with mutants as the dominant species.

NATHANIEL ESSEX
MISTER SINISTER

POWERS

Telepath. Shapeshifter. Superhuman strength

Mister Sinister has clones hidden everywhere. →

ORIGINS

Born in London in 1859, scientist Nathaniel Essex became obsessed with the idea of mutants and genetics. Apocalypse changed Nathaniel into Mister Sinister, a brooding villain who could alter his own genetic code. He has experimented on countless mutants and humans over the centuries. Sinister is very interested in the Summers DNA and has been lurking in the shadows during key events in Scott and Alex Summers' lives. Mister Sinister is a powerful mutant, and his genetic work means he has unlocked the secrets of human and mutant genomes.

HENRY 'HANK' MCCOY

BEAST

POWERS

Exceptional athleticism. Genius-level scientific mind. Increased senses.

Beast is an ambassador for mutantkind and was once an Avenger.

ORIGINS

There are few mutants who have mutated so much over their careers as Hank McCoy. The Beast who joined the first class of X-Men was a well-spoken young man with exceptionally large hands and feet, coupled with animal-like agility and athleticism. Over the years he has mutated further, first gaining blue fur, then a lion-like (and later ape-like) physical appearance coupled with heightened senses. Hank is the X-Men's resident genius in genetics, science and sarcastic remarks.

WARREN WORTHINGTON III

ANGEL

POWERS

Flight. Razor-sharp metal wings.

ORIGINS

Warren Worthington III comes from a wealthy family. He enrolled in Xavier's school when wings grew on his back. A member of the founding class of X-Men, Warren was in love with Jean Grey, but stepped away when he saw she had feelings for Scott. Angel's life was changed forever when Marauders captured him and damaged his wings. Warren was rebuilt by Apocalypse, who renamed him Archangel and gave him blue skin and organic metal wings. Though he returned to his original form, Warren has been caught in a battle between his Angel and Archangel personas ever since.

JAMES HOWLETT AKA LOGAN
WOLVERINE

POWERS

Heightened senses. Healing factor. Adamantium claws and skeleton.

Wolverine's unbreakable skeleton and claws were added by the Weapon X program.

ORIGINS

He's the best at what he does, but what he does isn't very nice. The X-Men's resident scrapper in now a mutant leader, but he is still an almost-unstoppable warrior with razor-sharp unbreakable claws and a healing factor that can negate any injury. Born over a hundred years ago in northern Canada, Wolverine has been a soldier, a government operative and has trained as a samurai, but nothing gave him inner peace until he joined the X-Men. Beneath his dark and brooding exterior Logan believes in Xavier's dream of peace, and has spent years teaching young mutants about their powers.

ORORO MUNROE
STORM

POWERS

Weather manipulation. Flight.

ORIGINS

Ororo is the daughter of a Kenyan princess who was orphaned and left on the street in Cario. When she tried to steal the wallet of Charles Xavier, he recognised the mutant potential in her and returned years later to offer her a place on a new X-Men team. Storm doesn't just rely on her mutant ability to manipulate the weather – her upbringing means that she is a skilled fighter in hand-to-hand combat. She has been a member of the Avengers and the Fantastic Four, but prefers to spend her time leading teams of X-Men.

N/A
SENTINELS

POWERS

Varies.

Sentinels usually only attack mutants, but they are a danger to the world as a whole.

ORIGINS

The shadow of the Sentinels has always fallen across the history of the X-Men. These giant, mutant-hunting robots exist in the present day, but many different time travellers have reported seeing them subjugating the mutant race in the future. The original Sentinels were created by Bolivar Trask, but other engineers have created their own versions and some are now self-replicating. There are many different types of Sentinel ranging from the microscopic nano-Sentinels to giant, spaceship-sized behemoths, but they are all the enemies of mutants and the X-Men.

MOJO
MOJO

POWERS

Reality manipulation in his home dimension.

ORIGINS

Wouldn't life be better if everything was more like a TV show? Mojo certainly thinks so, as his home dimension of the Mojoverse is completely based on broadcast television ratings. The X-Men of our dimension are very popular in Mojo's dimension, so he frequently kidnaps them, brainwashes them and forces them to act out his plots. Mojo is a ruthless despot who will genetically manipulate mutants if he thinks it will help his ratings, and he keeps an entire race of slaves to do his bidding.

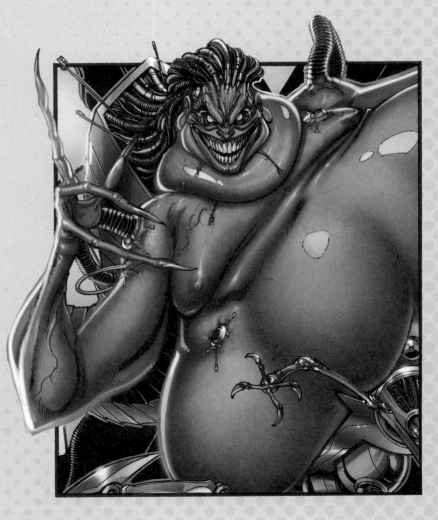

SHEN XORN, KUAN-YIN XORN
XORN

POWERS

Stars in their heads. Gravity manipulation. Telepathy. Teleportation. Magnetism.

ORIGINS

The Xorn brothers are two Chinese mutants whose power manifested as tiny stars inside their heads, and they were both imprisoned in metal masks as they learned to harness this awesome power. Kuan-Yin Xorn was approached by Cyclops to join the X-Men, where he was a powerful ally, before deciding that he was Magneto and fought the X-Men. Shen Xorn is equally powerful, and has struggled to find his place in the world.

The star in Xorn's head makes him one of the most powerful mutants in the world.

UNKNOWN
ARCADE

POWERS

Genius intelligence.

ORIGINS

For Arcade, everything is a game. He's smart enough that we don't know much about his history, but we do know that he is a deadly hitman who likes to place his victims in a series of elaborate deathtraps disguised as a theme park which he calls Murderworld. Each Murderworld is tailored specifically to the targets, and the X-Men have found themselves in deathtraps where their mutant powers were useless. Arcade doesn't appear to have any powers himself, but uses the technology of his Murderworlds to give him abilities like telekinesis and force field projection.

NATHAN SUMMERS
CABLE

POWERS

Telepathy. Telekinesis.
Superior firepower.

Cable's cyborg body is extremely tough.

ORIGINS

Cable is the time-displaced son of Scott Summers and Madelyne Pryor, and is actually much older than them. As an infant Nathan Summers was sent to the future to cure him of a techno-organic virus, where he was given a half-metal body and grew up fighting the forces of Apocalypse. An older and tougher Cable returned to the present day, where he became the leader of the New Mutants team, sending them into battle against the villain Stryfe, who turned out to be a clone of Cable himself. Growing up in a dystopian future made Cable tough, and he has trained other mutants to be just as uncompromising.

WADE WILSON
DEADPOOL

POWERS

Weapons training.
Near invulnerability
through healing factor.
Superhuman strength.

Deadpool's healing factor, training and smart mouth make him almost unstoppable.

ORIGINS

The merc with a mouth likes to pretend that he's a stone-cold killer, but under the wacky exterior lies a complicated moral code. Wade Wilson was a soldier from Canada who joined the Weapon X programme when he learned he had inoperable cancer. The programme unlocked his dormant mutant healing power, but covered him in disfiguring tumours. Deadpool's mutant healing factor allows him to survive any injury, which means that he takes almost nothing seriously and is constantly – *constantly* – wisecracking.

LUCAS BISHOP
BISHOP

POWERS

Energy absorption and redirection.

ORIGINS

Another member of the X-Men who grew up in an alternate future, Bishop is a mutant police officer who travelled back to the present day on the trail of dangerous criminals. Bishop's future is a dark place where mutants are branded and kept in camps, so he stays in the present day, trying to make sure that the future never comes to pass. Bishop is obsessed with stopping this awful future, and his quest sometimes puts him at odds with other X-Men.

Bishop was highly trained before he was sent back in time.

NEENA THURMAN
DOMINO

POWERS

Weapons training. Luck.

ORIGINS

Some people just have all the luck. Domino's mutant ability affects the probability fields of people in her line of sight, and she subconsciously gives herself good luck, too. Anyone who tries to attack her becomes extremely unlucky extremely fast. Domino was the product of a secret government programme to create a super weapon, but she escaped, first becoming a mercenary then later joining Cable's X-Force team. She doesn't just rely on her luck, she has advanced military combat and weapons training as well.

ST JOHN ALLERDYCE
PYRO

POWERS

Pyrokinesis.

ORIGINS

Some people just want to watch the world burn. The Australian mutant known as Pyro is able to control flames with his mind, and he carries a flamethrower on his back which feeds through to nozzles in his gauntlets. Recruited into the Brotherhood of Evil Mutants by Mystique, Pyro has fought the X-Men regularly for years. For a while he worked for the US government as part of Freedom Force, but this was mainly an excuse to harass the X-Men. He is a sadist and and murderer, and represents the dark side of the mutant race.

FRED DUKES
BLOB

POWERS

Superhuman strength.
Near impenetrable skin.
Can change his own gravity.

The Blob cannot be moved, but the ground that he is standing on can.

ORIGINS

Fred Dukes can manipulate his personal gravity field so that it is absolutely impossible to move him if he doesn't want to be moved. The Blob got his codename while working as a circus performer, using his mutant ability as a sideshow act. Professor X invited him to join the X-Men, but Dukes declined as he thought he was better than the X-Men. He eventually joined Magneto's Brotherhood of Evil Mutants. Blob is a cruel and unpleasant narcissist who enjoys hurting other people.

CAIN MARKO
JUGGERNAUT

POWERS

Superhuman strength and stamina. Almost unstoppable.

The Juggernaut claims to be unstoppable. He might just be right.

ORIGINS

The unstoppable force to Blob's immovable object, once Juggernaut builds up momentum it is virtually impossible to stop him. Cain Marko is Charles Xavier's half brother, who was given incredible powers by the demon Cyttorak. Marko found a gem in a hidden temple, and on touching it was transformed into a human juggernaut. He has completely wrecked the Xavier institute more than once and is one of the X-Men's most powerful villains as his helmet makes him immune to Charles Xavier's psychic attacks.

MORTIMER TOYNBEE
TOAD

POWERS

Prehensile tongue. Superhuman agility. Sticks to walls. Venomous spit.

ORIGINS

Toad was Magneto's main sycophant in the early days of the Brotherhood of Evil Mutants, but Toad always imagined that he had a strong relationship with the man he called master. Magneto's daughter, Scarlet Witch, was the object of Toad's affections, but she found him utterly repulsive. After Toad split from Magneto he was still obsessed with Wanda, and tried to kidnap her. Over the years Toad has been the leader of several villainous teams, but he always ends up being beaten by the X-Men.

KURT WAGNER
NIGHTCRAWLER

POWERS

Teleportation. Superhuman agility.

ORIGINS

Kurt Wagner grew up travelling with the Bavarian Circus after he was separated from his mother, Mystique. Local villagers became distrustful of his unusual appearance and ability to teleport, but as they came for him Nightcrawler was saved by Professor Xavier and given a place in the X-Men. Nightcrawler's good nature is much admired by his fellow X-Men and his demonic appearance is in stark contrast to his quiet and abiding religious beliefs.

Rogue retains the memories of people whose energy she has absorbed.

ANNA MARIE
ROGUE

POWERS

Energy and powers absorption through touch. Flight. Superhuman strength.

ORIGINS

Imagine living your whole life being afraid that if you touched another human being you might kill them. Rogue's mutant power sucks power, memories and energy from anyone she touches, and the first manifestation of her powers left her teenage boyfriend in a coma. She joined her adoptive mother Mystique in the Brotherhood of Evil Mutants, almost immediately fighting the Avengers and absorbing the powers and memories of Carol Danvers. Rogue was psychologically unable to deal with absorbing Danvers' personality and turned to Professor X for help. After he healed her she joined the X-Men.

REMY LEBEAU
GAMBIT

POWERS

Charges objects with explosive bio-kinetic energy.

ORIGINS

It took the other X-Men a while to trust Remy LeBeau because of his chequered past. Remy was a master thief who was reluctantly working with Mister Sinister and the Marauders. Storm helped him join the X-Men, where Gambit fell in love with Rogue. Although their romance was difficult at first due to the fact they couldn't touch, the two are now happily married. Gambit's mutant power allows him to charge objects with bio-kinetic energy which allows them to explode on contact. He carries a set of playing cards which he charges and uses as weapons.

Gambit can only charge inorganic objects, not living things.

PIOTR RASPUTIN
COLOSSUS

POWERS

Transforms body into organic steel.

ORIGINS

Piotr Rasputin's powers first manifested on the Siberian farm where he was born – as he was rushing to save his sister Illyana from a runaway tractor, Piotr's skin turned into unbreakable steel and protected him from the force of the tractor impact. When he first joined the X-Men Piotr found it hard to adjust to life in America, but he enjoyed spending time with fellow mutants, especially Kitty Pryde. Colossus is a true hero in every sense of the word, and would sacrifice himself for the greater good.

Piotr's organic steel skin may well be unbreakable.

VICTOR CREED

SABRETOOTH

POWERS

Heightened senses. Healing factor.
Retractable claws. Super strength.

Sabretooth has been fighting Wolverine for over 100 years.

ORIGINS

Wolverine's nemesis is a huge bully who was at one time part of the same government-run Weapon X programme as Logan. Like Logan, Creed is over a century old, and the two have been in each other's lives for decades, utterly despising the sight of each other. Sabretooth is a vicious man; he has killed for his government, he has killed for money and he has killed for pleasure. Like Wolverine, Sabretooth has incredibly acute animal-like senses and can track his prey (often Wolverine) for days.

ARKADY GREGORIVICH ROSSOVICH

OMEGA RED

POWERS

Carbonadium tentacles. Super strength.
Healing. Death Factor.

ORIGINS

Russia's mission to create their own version of Captain America didn't stop at the Red Guardian. Arkady Rossovich was a sociopathic killer before the KGB experimented on him. Now he has tentacles in his arms made from carbonadium, the Soviet equivalent of adamantium. Once he has caught his victim, Omega Red uses his mutant Death Factor to suck the life force from his prey while healing himself. Omega Red has a long running feud with Wolverine, and their combined healing factors mean their fights are long and painful.

YURIKO OYAMA
LADY DEATHSTRIKE

POWERS

Superhuman strength, stamina, agility.
Adamantium skeleton and claws. Healing factor.

ORIGINS

Yuriko Oyama's father was a crime boss called
Lord Dark Wind. He created the process of bonding
adamantium to bone that was used on Wolverine.
At first Yuriko wanted to atone for her father's
crimes, but later she was given adamantium bones
and razor-sharp claws, and became the super
criminal Lady Deathstrike. She joined a group of
criminal cyborgs known as the Reavers, replacing
any damaged parts of her body with technology.
Lady Deathstrike is a mercenary and assassin,
but she prides herself on the fact that she always
fights with honour.

AKHIRO HOWLETT
DAKEN

POWERS

Healing factor.
Retractable claws.

Daken has used the
Wolverine identity
in the past.

ORIGINS

For years Wolverine had no idea that he had a
son. Logan's pregnant wife, Itsu, was killed
by the Winter Soldier, but her unborn son was
saved. Despite this, Daken blames Logan for
abandoning him, and has tried to kill him many
times. Although Daken has Wolverine's claws,
healing factor and advanced senses, he has none
of his compassion, heroism or nobility. He is a
clever and wily manipulator who enjoys causing
pain to others, both physically and emotionally.

VILLAINS

93

ILLYANA RASPUTIN

MAGIK

POWERS

Inter-dimensional teleportation. Magic. Soulsword.

ORIGINS

Piotr Rasputin's younger sister was extremely proud of her brother joining the X-Men, but after coming to live with him in America she was captured by the demon Belasco and taken to the Limbo dimension. Illyana learned to harness her mutant powers of sorcery and created a Soulsword, a blade forged with the energy from her own soul. She then took over the dimension, driving Belasco away. Spending so much time in Limbo has psychically scarred Magik, and she is a much darker person than the carefree child that Colossus once knew.

EMMA FROST

THE WHITE QUEEN

POWERS

High-level psychic. Converts to organic diamond form.

Emma Frost will do whatever it takes to help the mutant race, and herself.

ORIGINS

Once one of the X-Men's greatest villains, Emma Frost was the White Queen in the notorious Hellfire Club, where she schemed to destroy the X-Men. Since leaving the club she has changed her life, becoming a teacher at the Xavier institute. Her cold and haughty demeanor hides a noble heart, which is why Charles Xavier asked her to join his school. Emma is a top-level psychic and her secondary mutation allows her to convert her entire body to an organic diamond form.

KITTY PRYDE
SHADOWCAT

POWERS

Intangibility.

ORIGINS

Life is always hard for the youngest students at the Xavier Institute, and Kitty Pryde joined the X-Men when she was only 13-years-old. Kitty has grown to be a wise and perceptive teacher and leader of young mutants – she's come a long way from the young woman who thought Professor Xavier was a jerk. Shadowcat's phasing ability allows her to walk through solid objects, and she can disrupt the electrical activity of anything she passes through. Kitty is exceptionally clever and is a genius-level computer scientist.

Kitty Pryde is a natural leader, but has come into conflict with other X-Men.

JUBILATION LEE
JUBILEE

POWERS

Pyrokinetic energy blasts.

ORIGINS

One of the brightest and sparkiest of the X-Men, Jubilee's mutant ability allows her to generate plasma 'fireworks' from her hands, which detonate with varying levels of intensity. Jubilee joined the X-Men after her parents were killed, and her natural abilities as a gymnast served the team well. Wolverine and Jubilee were always close, and Jubilee saw him as a kind of father figure. Jubilee's natural levity often helped to lift Logan's natural gruffness. She has been on many X-Men teams and has grown into a leadership position.

DAVID HALLER
LEGION

POWERS

Reality manipulation.

Each of David Haller's personalities have different powers, and theoretically he can do anything.

ORIGINS

David Haller has possibly limitless mutant powers and very severe mental health issues. He is the son of Charles Xavier and Gabrielle Haller, but Professor X was initially unaware that he had a child. David's mental illness manifests itself as dissociative identity disorder, with different personalities having completely different mutant powers. The combination of mutant powers is truly staggering, with different aspects of Legion being able to travel in time and even rewrite reality itself. David's tragedy is that he may never fully control his powers, and he knows how dangerous that makes him.

AMAHL FAROUK
SHADOW KING

POWERS

Powerful psychic. Immortal. Can possess bodies. Telepath.

ORIGINS

The exact origins of the Shadow King are unknown, but he claims to be the manifestation of the dark side of mankind. For years he lived in Cairo, where he took the form of Egyptian crime lord Amahl Farouk, which is where he met and battled Charles Xavier. The Shadow King is an Omega-level psychic who takes over people's bodies and controls them like a puppet master. Farouk is so powerful that when he was killed by Charles Xavier he simply moved to the Astral Plane, and existed as a disembodied essence.

SEBASTIAN SHAW
BLACK KING

POWERS

Energy absorption and conversion.

ORIGINS

The Hellfire Club is a shadowy secret society, bent on taking over the world. Sebastian Shaw was already a self-made billionaire when he joined the Hellfire Club, and soon he became the leader, killing anyone who got in his way. Hellfire Club leaders have codenames based on chess pieces, and Shaw is the Black King. Sebastian Shaw's plans for world domination have brought him into conflict with the X-Men many times, but as a mutant he has claimed his place on the Island of Krakoa.

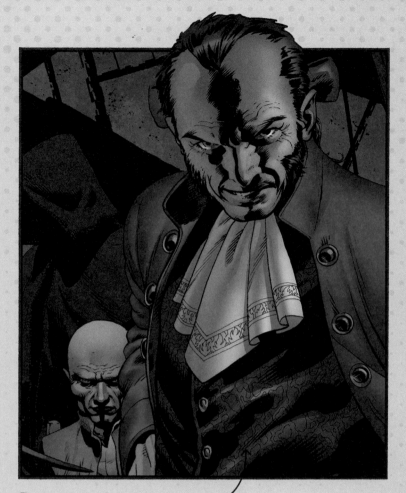

Emma Frost and Sebastian Shaw have an uneasy alliance.

MADELYNE PRYOR
MADELYNE PRYOR

POWERS

Telepath. Telekinetic. High-level psychic.

ORIGINS

After Jean Grey died, Scott Summers thought he would never love again. Then he met Madelyne Pryor, a pilot who bore an uncanny resemblance to Jean. Scott and Madelyne married, and Madelyne gave birth to Nathan Summers, who would later become Cable. In fact, Madelyne was a clone of Jean Grey, created by Mister Sinister. After the real Jean Grey came back to life, Madelyne's psychic powers emerged and she became evil, fighting the X-Men as the mad Goblyn Queen. Although she appeared to die in a climactic battle with Jean Grey, Madelyne has since reappeared.

VILLAINS

RACHEL SUMMERS AKA RACHEL GREY
RACHEL SUMMERS

POWERS

Telepathy. Telekinesis. Empathy.

ORIGINS

There are so many mutants from dystopian futures that it's hard to keep track of them all. Rachel is the daughter of Scott Summers and Jean Grey, who grew up in a future where the Mutant Registration Act was passed. In this future, mutants were hunted down by other mutants and sent to mutant concentration camps. Rachel was one of these hunters. She managed to travel back in time to the present day, but she finds it hard to hide from the memories of the awful things she has done.

Rachel Summers' tattoos denote her as a mutant hunter.

ALISON BLAIRE
DAZZLER

POWERS

Converts sound into light and energy.

ORIGINS

There aren't very many super heroes who are also famous pop stars. Dazzler's mutant ability to turn sound into light and energy beams means that she always puts on an incredible show for her audience. Alison Blaire's popularity has made her a great, high-profile ambassador for mutants in human culture, and she has also been an agent of S.H.I.E.L.D. Although her music career has been successful at times, Dazzler has always returned to her mutant family in the X-Men.

JEAN-PAUL BEAUBIER
NORTHSTAR

POWERS

Flight. Superhuman speed and durability.
Light manipulation.

ORIGINS

An Olympic-medal-winning Candadian skier, Jean-Paul Beaubier's mutant powers of flight and superspeed made any sport easy for him. Originally a member of Canadian super hero team Alpha Flight, Northstar joined the X-Men after his original team were disbanded. Jean-Paul has a twin sister, Jeanne-Marie, who goes by the codename Aurora – she was briefly a member of the X-Men, but left due to her struggles with personality disorders.

SEAN CASSIDY
BANSHEE

POWERS

Flight.
Sonic scream.

Banshee's sonic scream is poweful enough to shatter stone.

ORIGINS

The father of fellow X-Man Syrin, Banshee is an Irish national who was an Interpol Police Officer before joining the X-Men. Sean Cassidy's cousin is Black Tom Cassidy, another mutant who often teams up with the Juggernaut to cause trouble. Banshee's mutant power allows him to emit a sonic scream that he can use to attack his enemies or allow himself to fly. One of the team of mutants who rescued the original X-Men from Krakoa, Banshee has acted as a mentor for several younger teams.

(NO REAL NAME)
DANGER

POWERS

Energy projection. Holographic projection. Superhuman strength and durability.

ORIGINS

The Danger Room was the pride of Charles Xavier's school – a holographic training room which could create any situation to test the mutant powers of the X-Men. Eventually the Danger Room gained sentience and turned against the X-Men, calling herself Danger. Danger could use all the holographic and energy-based powers of the Danger Room, and knew all the X-Men's strengths and weaknesses. Despite being angry at Professor X for imprisoning her, Danger has since formed an alliance with the X-Men.

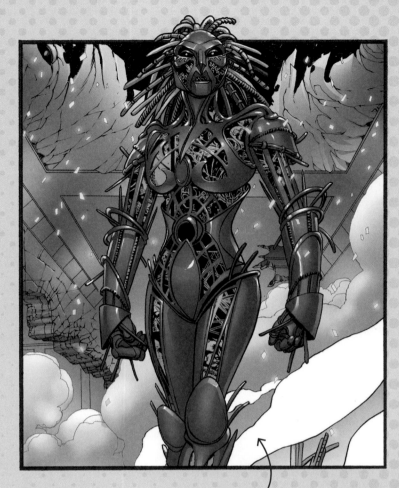

Danger knows the fight patterns of everyone who has trained in the Danger Room.

CASSANDRA NOVA
CASSANDRA NOVA

POWERS

Top-level psychic. Mind control. Shapeshifting.

ORIGINS

Cassandra Nova claimed that she was Charles Xavier's twin sister, killed in the womb but given form. In reality she is something more complicated – a mummudrai, a psychic parasite from the astral plane. She became psychically linked to Xavier which gave her the ability to create her own body by copying Xavier's DNA. Cassandra is everything that Charles is not – a murderer who is obsessed with destruction, she once commanded an army of Sentinels to murder 16 million mutants in Genosha.

KARL LYKOS
SAURON

POWERS

Flight. Energy vampire.
Fire breath. Hypnotism.

ORIGINS

Karl Lykos was a normal human who was bitten by a mutant pterodactyl on a visit to the Savage Land. He found that he was now an energy vampire who needed to drain the life force of others to survive. When he absorbed the energy of Havok he transformed into a humanoid pterodactyl creature. Mutant energy is especially potent for Sauron as it allows him to transform between his human and dinosaur forms. Sauron is the leader of the Mutates in the Savage Land, and has fought the X-Men and Spider-Man many times.

Sauron is a brillaint scientist and can alter a subject's genetic material.

RITA WAYWORD
SPIRAL

POWERS

Multiple arms.
Teleportation. Magic.

Spiral's six arms mean that she is deadly in armed combat.

ORIGINS

Stuntwoman Rita Wayword was attacked by someone who would be revealed to be her future self. To protect her, her friend Longshot took Rita to his home dimension of Mojoverse where she was captured by Mojo and genetically altered. Now called Spiral, she has multiple arms, training in sorcery and the ability to see across time and dimensions. This manipulation drove Spiral quite mad, and she travelled back in time, trying unsuccessfully to kill Longshot and her former self. She is displaced in time, an unwitting accomplice in her own tragic origin story.

ALEX SUMMERS
HAVOK

POWERS

Energy absorption and discharge.

ORIGINS

The younger brother of Cyclops, Alex has never found being a super hero as easy as Scott. Havok's power allows him to absorb energy then release it as a blast of super hot plasma. At first Alex found it hard to control his powers, but he soon earned a place in the X-Men, fighting alongside his brother. Havok has led X-Men teams, and even led an Avengers team, but has often spent time away from super hero life with his on-again/off-again girlfriend Polaris.

Alex is an outsider, which is why he gets on so well with Wolverine.

LORNA DANE
POLARIS

POWERS

Magnetism.

ORIGINS

The green-haired Polaris always suspected that Magneto was her father, but this was not confirmed until she was an adult. Like her father, Lorna is a mutant who can control magnetic fields and manipulate metals. Lorna Dane has a longstanding and complicated romantic relationship with Havok; the two were engaged but never married. The pressure of being an X-Man and the daughter of Magneto has taken its toll on Lorna, and she has struggled with mental health issues, sometimes acting erratically or dangerously.

JAMIE MADROX
MULTIPLE MAN

POWERS

Creates duplicates
of himself.

ORIGINS

Jamie Madrox has always been his own best
friend. He has the power to create copies of
himself, or 'dupes' as he calls them, all with the
same powers and separate – often competing –
personalities. The original Jamie calls himself
Jamie Prime and can absorb the knowledge and
skills of any dupes, meaning that he is an expert
in kung fu, espionage, firearms, law and medicine.
Jamie has sent out duplicates of himself all over
the world, and has seemingly died several times,
only for another duplicate of him to be found. This
is extremely confusing for the X-Men.

Each of Jamie's
duplicates has a
different personality.

LONGSHOT
LONGSHOT

POWERS

Luck. Superhuman
speed and agility.

Longshot only has
three fingers and
thumbs, but is an
expert marksman.

ORIGINS

Longshot was created through genetic
engineering on the Mojoworld dimension, but he
escaped and fled to our world where he became
allied with the X-Men. As an artificially-created
life-form, Longshot's physiology is unique: he has
two hearts, superhuman speed and agility and
damage-resistant skin. His special power allows
him to affect probability and he is literally luckier
than anyone else, but it only works when Longshot
is feeling confident and heroic. It does not work
for selfish or evil acts.

CHAPTER EIGHT
THE FANTASTIC FOUR

NICK FURY'S NOTES

The Fantastic Four feel like they're part of your own family. They might argue and bicker, but every family argues and bickers, and it makes us feel even closer to them. There's something about the Fantastic Four that you like — that you want to trust.

Which is why I need to periodically remind myself of how powerful these beings are. Reed Richards has created devices that can cross time and space. Johnny Storm is powerful enough to destroy New York City. I still don't know the upper limit of Ben Grimm's strength. Susan Richards could be in the room with you right now.

I can't afford to take my eye off the Fantastic Four.

REED RICHARDS
MISTER FANTASTIC

POWERS

Elasticity. Super genius.

Reed Richards' inventions have saved the Earth on countless occasions.

ORIGINS

Reed Richards' body is as elastic and malleable as his brilliant mind. The Fantastic Four got their powers when Reed Richards led the team on a mission into space where they were blasted by cosmic rays, changing them forever. As the leader of the Fantastic Four, Reed Richards has taken the team on countless adventures across time, space and dimensions, using his brilliant inventions to save the day time and time again. He is one of the world's greatest scientists, but Reed will always place his family above all else.

SUSAN STORM RICHARDS
INVISIBLE WOMAN

POWERS

Invisibility. Invisible shields, force fields and constructs.

Sue Storm's powers allow her to go nearly anywhere and do nearly anything.

ORIGINS

In terms of raw power, Susan Storm Richards is the strongest member of the Fantastic Four. She can make herself invisible, and can create invisible force fields and weapons that are limited only by her willpower. Sue Storm was in love with Reed Richards before the fateful voyage that gave them their powers, and the two were married after becoming super heroes. Reed and Sue have two children, Franklin and Valeria. Sue often acts as the mother figure of the team and while the Fantastic Four may argue like any other family, they will stick together through anything.

BENJAMIN GRIMM
THE THING

POWERS

Super strength and stamina.
Rock-hard orange skin.

ORIGINS

Ben Grimm often sees himself as the super strong muscle of the Fantastic Four, but he is so much more. The Thing is the heart of the group, with his fragile humanity hidden under his rock-hard exterior. Ben was Reed's pilot and Reed sees his inability to find a cure for Ben's condition as his greatest scientific failure. Born in the impoverished Yancy Street in New York, Ben will never forget his roots and always returns to his old neighbourhood.

The upper limit of Ben Grimm's strength is still in contention.

JOHNNY STORM
HUMAN TORCH

POWERS

Pyrokinesis. Flight.
Creates flames that
cover his body.

Johnny Storm can create enough heat to cause his body to go into a 'supernova' state.

ORIGINS

Johnny Storm is a hothead in more ways than one. The younger brother of Sue Storm, he was raised by his sister after their parents died. Cosmic rays gave Johnny the ability to cover his body with fiery plasma, and control any flame in his vicinity. The youngest member of the Fantastic Four, Johnny is brash and reckless, and is easily distracted by fast cars and beautiful women. Johnny is a hero to his core, and has saved the world more times than he can probably remember.

VICTOR VON DOOM
DOCTOR DOOM

POWERS

Scientific genius. Master of sorcery.
Technologically advanced suit of armour.

ORIGINS

The proud and haughty Victor Von Doom grew up in the Balkan country of Latveria, but came to America to study at Empire State University where he was roommates with Reed Richards. Victor created a machine to talk to his dead mother, but the machine exploded, scarring him for life. Blaming Richards for his own mistake, Doom now wears a suit of metal armour, and rules his homeland of Latveria with an iron fist. After fighting the Fantastic Four for years, Doom studied sorcery and is now a powerful magician as well as being a cutting-edge technologist.

Doom's real strength is his complete inability to ever back down.

HARVEY ELDER
MOLE MAN

POWERS

Heightened senses.
Genius.

Mole Man commands an army of massive monsters.

ORIGINS

Deep below the earth there is a huge, underground realm called Subterranea, which is the home of a vast range of outlandish creatures. Harvey Elder is an explorer who found Subterranea and became the ruler of a race called the Moloids, calling himself Mole Man. He is obsessed with how the surface world has mistreated him, and regularly sends large monsters to attack the surface – especially New York. The Fantastic Four have beaten him back many times, forging fragile truces between Subterranea and our world.

OWEN REECE
MOLECULE MAN

POWERS

Can change reality
at will.

Molecule Man's powers have had an adverse affect on his sanity.

ORIGINS

Is Molecule Man the most powerful person in the universe? He can control the very building blocks of the universe, right down to the molecular level. Once a lab technician from Brooklyn, Owen Reece was subjected to an unknown radiation which gave him his incredible powers. He immediately tried to take over Manhattan, but was eventually stopped by the Fantastic Four and transported to another dimension. It's possible that Molecule Man cannot die, and he has even rebuilt himself from almost nothing in the past. Owen Reece has battled toe-to-toe with cosmic entities and only seems to be getting more powerful.

ANNIHILUS
ANNIHILUS

POWERS

Superhuman strength, speed. Flight.
Cosmic Control Rod.

ORIGINS

When the Fantastic Four first entered the Negative Zone, a dark dimension close to ours, they encountered its ruler, Annihilus. The Negative Zone is a cold, unforgiving place, and Annihilus is a paranoid, despotic ruler. Using his immensely powerful Cosmic Control Rod, Annihilus commands hordes of alien insectoids. Recently Annihilus has led a huge fleet of spaceships called the Annihilation Wave from the Negative Zone with the objective of destroying or controlling as many planets as possible, and was only stopped by Galactus himself.

FRANKLIN RICHARDS
FRANKLIN RICHARDS

POWERS

Reality manipulation. Universe creation. High-level psychic powers. Immortality.

There is a rumour that Franklin Richards will be alive at the end of the universe, he is that powerful.

ORIGINS

The son of Reed Richards and Susan Storm is one of the most powerful mutants that will ever live. Growing up with the Fantastic Four means that Franklin has always wanted to be a super hero, but apart from that he is surprisingly well-adjusted. Franklin has been captured by many major super villains, but he has always managed to escape. His awesome powers allow him to warp reality and read minds. Franklin's power levels mean that he is immortal, and at the end of the universe there will only be Franklin and Galactus left.

VALERIA RICHARDS
VALERIA RICHARDS

POWERS

Genius-level intelligence.

ORIGINS

The sixth member of the Fantastic Four, Valeria is the smarter younger sister of Franklin Richards. Valeria birth was complicated, and Sue and Reed were forced to ask Doctor Doom to help them deliver Valeria into the world. Victor agreed, but only if they named her after his mother, Valeria. Though she is only a child, her father Reed Richards thinks that she is already more intelligent than he is. Valeria loves her family and spends a good deal of time getting her brother Franklin out of trouble.

NAMOR

NAMOR, THE SUBMARINER

POWERS

Superhuman strength, durability and speed. Flight.

Namor has spent as much time fighting the surface world as he has saving it.

ORIGINS

Namor is the son of an Atlantean princess and a sea captain. For years he led a campaign of terror against the surface world, trying to destroy humans for committing crimes against his undersea people. During World War II he became a hero and fought alongside Captain America. After the war he wandered, lost in an amnesiac state, before the Fantastic Four found him and helped him regain his memories. The king of Atlantis is the first mutant – he is the only Atlantean to be able to fly.

CRYSTALIA AMAQUELIN

CRYSTAL

POWERS

Elemental manipulation. Flight. Super strength.

ORIGINS

Crystal is a member of the Inhumans, a race of super-powered beings who have technology well in advance of our own. A princess in the Inhuman Royal Family, Crystal met and fell in love with Johnny Storm, and briefly joined the Fantastic Four as a member. Crystal left the Human Torch and married Quicksilver from the X-Men, although their marriage has been somewhat rocky. Crystal has been an Avenger as well as a member of the Fantastic Four, but her first loyalty is to the Inhumans.

UNKNOWN
MAD THINKER

POWERS

Genius-level intellect.

ORIGINS

Like Reed Richards, the Mad Thinker is a genius, but unlike Reed Richards he uses his powers for personal gain, and has been trying to take over the world for years. He uses advanced robots to do his bidding, including the Awesome Android – a super tough robot who can mimic other creatures' abilities after touching them. The Mad Thinker has a large collection of android replicas of himself and can project his consciousness into them, so that even when his body is incarcerated in prison, he can walk free in an android shell.

The Mad Thinker has hidden collections of powerful, deadly androids.

PETER PETRUSKI
TRAPSTER

POWERS

Special glue guns. Explosives and weapons in suite.

ORIGINS

Peter Petruski is a chemist and career criminal who has designed a variety of different glue and adhesive devices to help him steal and avoid capture. Initially calling himself Paste-Pot Pete, he ran foul of the Human Torch when he tried to steal a military missile. Vowing revenge, he joined the Frightful Four, a team of villains organised by the Wizard to attack the Fantastic Four. The Trapster has a suit packed full of different gadgets including explosives, weapons and glues, and, true to his name, he likes to use them to trap his opponents.

KL'RT
SUPER-SKRULL

POWERS

Pyrokinesis. Super strength. Invisibility. Elasticity. Invisible constructs.

ORIGINS

The Skrulls are a race of shape-changing aliens who have tried to invade the Earth several times, but have been stopped by Earth's heroes including the Fantastic Four. Kl'rt is a Skrull soldier who blames the Fantastic Four for his race's defeat, and was given the powers of each of the Fantastic Four as a way to destroy them. Though he is fiery, elastic, invisible and strong, the Super-Skrull has none of the teamwork, ingenuity and drive that make the Fantastic Four so brilliant.

The Super-Skrull is bound by honour, which may be his weakness. ↘

UNKNOWN
IMPOSSIBLE MAN

POWERS

Shapeshifting. Teleportation.

ORIGINS

The Impossible Man isn't so much a villain as a super-powered prankster who is desperate for attention. An alien from the planet Poppup in the Tenth Galaxy, he can change his shape to almost any form, in ways that should be impossible. He is an expert on Earth's popular culture and takes very little in life seriously. The Impossible Man first met the Fantastic Four when he was on holiday on our planet, and was only defeated when they ignored him and he went away.

BLACKAGAR BOLTAGON
BLACK BOLT

POWERS

Flight. Vocal chords are powerful enough to create physical blasts.

Even a whisper from Black Bolt can shatter a mountain.

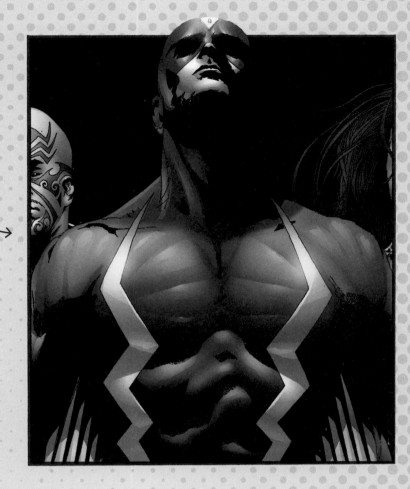

ORIGINS

The king of the Inhumans is a man of few words, mainly because his voice is so powerful that it can level cities. Not being able to converse would hinder most rulers, but Black Bolt communicates through his wife Medusa. Although Black Bolt is a wise and fair ruler his evil brother Maximus is constantly trying to usurp him, using any means necessary to take the crown. Inhumans are naturally distrustful of humans, but Black Bolt has formed close friendships with the Fantastic Four and the Avengers.

MEDUSALITH AMAQUELIN-BOLTAGAN
MEDUSA

POWERS

Prehensile hair. Superhuman strength, stamina.

ORIGINS

Black Bolt's wife is the only person who has been both a member of the super hero group Fantastic Four and the super villain team Frightful Four. Medusa is an Inhuman who suffered amnesia when she was attacked by Black Bolt's brother Maximus, and was tricked into joining the Wizard's evil team. Once she had regained her memories she married Black Bolt, and helped him rule the Inhumans, taking breaks to adventure with the Fantastic Four. Medusa has incredibly strong, powerful hair that she can command at will.

KARNAK MANDER-AZUR
KARNAK

POWERS

Master of martial arts. Can find any weakness.

ORIGINS

Karnak's greatest ability is also his greatest curse – he can find the weakness in absolutely anything. This power makes him a devastating martial artist, capable of incapacitating an opponent with a single blow. He is known as 'the Shatterer' by Inhumans because of his abilitiy to destroy an object by exploiting its faults. Karnak can also be morose and withdrawn, seeing only weaknesses in the world, but he is a gifted puzzle-solver and a trusted advisor to Black Bolt.

Karnak gained his powers from study and reflection, not from the Inhuman's terrigen mists.

LOCKJAW
LOCKJAW

POWERS

Teleportation.

ORIGINS

When the Inhumans want to travel large distances they use their huge teleporting dog, Lockjaw. Though he is no more intelligent than a normal dog, Lockjaw is a loyal companion to the Inhuman Royal Family, acting as their protector as well as their means of transport. He is fond of the Fantastic Four and is always especially pleased to see Ben Grimm. Lockjaw once formed his own team of Pet-Avengers, including Falcon's bird Redwing and a frog version of Thor called Throg.

MARY MACPHERRAN
TITANIA

POWERS

Upper-level superhuman strength and stamina.

ORIGINS

Not only is Titania physically strong enough to battle the Thing, Thor and She-Hulk, she's also emotionally strong enough to have remained married to the Absorbing Man for years, while both of them struggle with lives in and outside prison. Mary MacPherran got her powers when she was unwittingly swept up in a cosmic super hero battle, and was given top-level strength and stamina by Doctor Doom himself. Titania has tried to go straight and work for the government in the past, but the super villain life is hard to leave behind.

PHILLIP MASTERS
PUPPET MASTER

POWERS

Uses radioactive clay to create puppets which he uses to control people.

The Puppet Master's clay comes from the mysterious Mount Wundagore.

ORIGINS

Phillip Masters is the stepfather of Ben Grimm's wife Alicia Masters and also one of the Fantastic Four's oldest enemies. Masters has access to a special type of radioactive (and possibly magical) clay that he fashions into marionettes of real people, and then he uses the puppets to control them. The Puppet Master is a master of manipulation and loves to control events from the shadows – he is a bitter and vengeful villain and should not be trusted.

BENTLEY WHITTMAN
WIZARD

POWERS

Genius. Sleight of hand expert. Mind control via helmet.

ORIGINS

A genius inventor and stage magician, Bentley Whittman tried to inject some excitement into his life by attacking the Fantastic Four. After being beaten by the Human Torch, the Wizard has created several different teams called the Frightful Four, all with the express intention of destroying the Richards family. Though he has no powers, Bentley Whittman is a highly advanced scientist and inventor, equalling Reed Richards himself. A teenage clone of the Wizard called Bentley-23 is currently living with the Fantastic Four's Future Foundation.

Bentley Whittman is obsessed with the Fantastic Four and will do anything to destroy them.

DRAGON MAN
DRAGON MAN

POWERS

Superhumanly strong android body. Flight. Fire breath.

ORIGINS

Dragon Man is an android who was brought to life using alchemy and supernatural powers. At first Dragon Man had only limited intelligence and was unable to talk, attacking the Fantastic Four when ordered to do so. His tough android body and ability to breathe fire made him a formidable opponent for the Fantastic Four. More recently he has been reprogrammed by Valeria Richards to have super intelligence. He is a helpful, wise and verbose android, protecting the children of the Future Foundation.

CHAPTER NINE
GUARDIANS OF THE GALAXY
AND COSMIC HEROES

NICK FURY'S NOTES

I hate cosmic battles. Everything takes place light years away from Earth, so I never hear about anything until it's already over, by which point there's nothing I can do about it. Or the other way these things work is that everything is quiet for years, then suddenly aliens are walking through Times Square in New York with no warning.

My files should be current and accurate, but the universe is a big place and it's not always easy to keep track of the major players, especially when they keep blowing each other up. I hate cosmic battles.

PETER QUILL
STAR-LORD

POWERS

Enhanced strength and durability. Flight via rocket boots. Marksman.

Quill is only half-human, but he grew up on Earth.

ORIGINS

Nobody believes in Peter Quill quite as much as Peter Quill. Star-Lord is the son of J'Son, an alien ruler who crash-landed on Earth. Peter has had an exciting life – he was a NASA pilot who was captured by Ravagers and escaped, travelling the galaxy looking for adventure. The latest Guardians of the Galaxy team was formed by Star-Lord as a proactive way to deal with emerging threats, and while unconventional, they can almost always be counted on to save the day.

ROCKET RACCOON
ROCKET

POWERS

Skilled marksman. Tactician. Heightened senses.

ORIGINS

Rocket comes from the planet Halfworld, where he was genetically altered to have human-level intelligence and be able to stand on two feet. He may be small, but Rocket makes sure that he always has access to a large gun or an inappropriate amount of explosives and is famously trigger-happy. He is the weapons and tactics expert for the Guardians of the Galaxy, and he steps up and leads the team when Star-Lord isn't around.

Rocket's speciality is in inappropriately destructive weaponry.

HE IS GROOT
GROOT

POWERS

Superhuman strength. Can grow and regenerate plant body.

ORIGINS

This sentient alien tree first came to Earth years ago as part of an invasion force, but he now fights to protect the galaxy. Groot is a Flora Colossus from the Planet X, and his unevolved vocal chords make it sound to the untrained ear as if he is repeating the phrase 'I am Groot' when he is talking. Thankfully the Guardians can understand what he is saying. Rocket and Groot have a special bond, with Rocket caring for Groot when he needs to regrow.

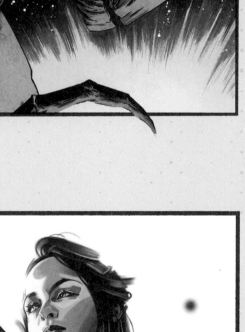

Groot can regrow himself from just a single twig.

GAMORA
GAMORA

POWERS

Combat training. Superhuman strength, speed and agility.

ORIGINS

The last member of the Zen-Whoberis race, Gamora was taken in as a child by Thanos and trained to be a living weapon. The deadliest woman in the galaxy, Gamora has now turned against her adoptive father and tries to use her exceptional fighting abilities for good as a member of the Guardians of the Galaxy. Gamora was once a member of Adam Warlock's Infinity Watch and for a while was trapped in the Soul Stone.

THANOS

THANOS

POWERS

Superhuman strength, stamina and speed. Genius-level intelligence.

Thanos is a threat to every single being in the galaxy.

ORIGINS

The name Thanos is known throughout the universe as it belongs to the deadliest villain who has ever lived. Born on Titan to the race of Eternals, Thanos worshipped Mistress Death, killing millions of his own race to impress her. Thanos has spent his life searching for more and more powerful ways to kill, once collecting all six Infinity Stones and nearly wiping out half of all life in the universe. He is terrifying because of his genius, power and single-minded obsession with death.

NEBULA

NEBULA

POWERS

Combat training. Superhuman strength, speed and agility.

ORIGINS

Gamora's adopted sister was trained by Thanos to be a deadly warrior, and the two were often set against each other in combat. Nebula fell out of favour with Thanos and for years roamed the galaxy as a space pirate, taking what she wanted by force or by cunning. Though she has tried to redeem herself, Nebula's dysfunctional childhood makes it very hard for her to trust anyone, and she still sees violence as the answer to most problems.

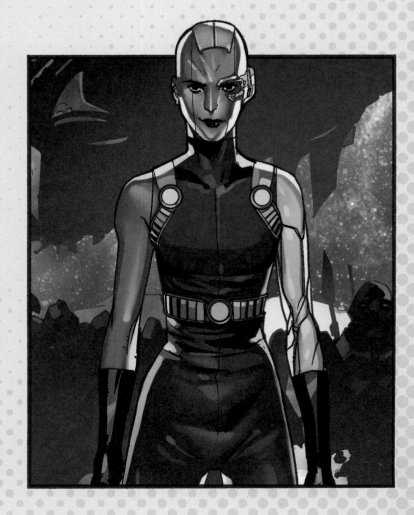

RONAN
RONAN THE ACCUSER

POWERS

Combat training. Superhuman strength, speed and agility. Universal Weapon.

ORIGINS

The Supreme Accuser is one of the highest titles in the Kree empire, and Ronan takes his position very seriously. Ronan wields a Universal Weapon which can fire cosmic energy as well as allowing him to teleport and fly. He is single-minded in his devotion to the Kree, and will do anything if he thinks is it for the good of the empire. Ronan was married to Crystal, as a way of forging a bond between Inhumans and Kree, and although the two did not love each other at first, they were sad when the marriage ended.

EN DWI GAST
THE GRANDMASTER

POWERS

Immortality. Matter manipulation. Energy blasts.

ORIGINS

Everything is a game to the Grandmaster. He is one of the powerful and eccentric Elders of the Universe who have existed since the dawn of history and use the Power Primordial. The Grandmaster has mastered all games in the universe and loves to pit opposing teams against each other and bet on the outcome. Many of Earth's heroes have been abducted by the Grandmaster and forced through different types of gauntlets and challenges.

Even though he is impossibly powerful, the Grandmaster is bound to play by his own rules.

ARTHUR DOUGLAS
DRAX THE DESTROYER

POWERS

Superhuman strength, stamina and speed. Combat training.

As a human, Arthur Douglas loved to play saxaphone.

ORIGINS

Drax the Destroyer was once an Earth man named Arthur Douglas who, along with his wife, was killed by Thanos. Douglas was placed in a powerful new body by the Titan god Kronos and sent on a mission to kill Thanos. Drax has been helping to stop Thanos' plans for years. He acted alone at first, then as a member of Adam Warlock's Infinity Watch and later as part of Star-Lord's Guardians of the Galaxy. He has been through a lot of hardship in his life, which is reflected in his serious and gruff demeanor.

HEATHER DOUGLAS
MOONDRAGON

POWERS

Telekinesis. Telepathy. Master martial artist.

Moondragon is highly erratic, and has fought the Avengers.

ORIGINS

When Thanos killed Drax's wife, Drax thought his daughter had also died. In fact, Heather Douglas was taken to Titan by Mentor, Thanos' father, and trained in martial arts by monks. Heather was trained to tap into her latent psionic powers and she became a powerful psychic. Moondragon has been both a friend and a foe to the Avengers, as her temper and sense of her own importance can sometimes get the better of her. She takes her name from the Dragon of the Moon, an ancient threat that she has been psychically fighting ever since she got her powers.

COSMO

COSMO THE SPACEDOG

POWERS

Telepathy. Telekinesis. Mind blasts.

ORIGINS

Before they sent humans into space, the early Soviet space programme sent animals up in space ships. Cosmo was sent into Earth's orbit but was mutated by cosmic rays, giving him a range of psychic powers including telekinesis, telepathy, psychic shields and mind blasts. He ended up on Knowhere, the city built in the head of a dead Celestial, where he became the Security Chief. He assisted the Guardians of the Galaxy when they operated out of Knowhere, but does not want to leave the station.

UNKNOWN

MANTIS

POWERS

Telepathy. Empathy. Can converse with plants. Martial arts training.

ORIGINS

Mantis was born in Vietnam, but was trained by alien Kree monks in martial arts. Her skin turned green when she merged with the alien plant species called the Cotati, which gave her limited telepathy, the ability to feel others' emotions and the ability to talk to plants. Mantis joined the Avengers along with the reformed villain Swordsman, but did not stay in the team long. More recently she has joined the Guardians of the Galaxy, serving as an unofficial counsellor to the group.

CORVUS GLAIVE
CORVUS GLAIVE

POWERS

Superhuman strength, speed.
Weapon can cut through anything.

ORIGINS

The Black Order are Thanos' most trusted and most ruthless warriors, helping him in his path of pain and destruction. Corvus Glaive is Thanos' most favoured and acts as his second-in-command, carrying out the most violent and horrific of orders. Corvus is cruel and arrogant, but he is also ambitious and has formed his own version of the Black Order when Thanos is absent. His weapon, a glaive, gives him strength and immortality and it can cut through absolutely anything in the universe.

The Black Order have carved a swathe of destruction through the galaxy.

EBONY MAW
EBONY MAW

Ebony Maw is powerful enough to control the mind of Stephen Strange.

POWERS

Telekinesis. Telepathy.
Mind control. Flight.
Genius.

ORIGINS

The most dangerous member of Thanos' Black Order isn't much of a fighter at all, and tends to avoid direct confrontations. Ebony Maw likes to work behind the scenes, manipulating his prey through his psychic powers, exceptional intelligence and raw cunning. He is a vicious and sadistic operator, often playing with his victims for his own personal amusement while he carries out his orders. Ebony Maw is not to be trusted and will betray absolutely anyone, including his master, Thanos.

PROXIMA MIDNIGHT
PROXIMA MIDNIGHT

POWERS

Superhuman strength, speed. Invulnerable.

ORIGINS

Proxima Midnight is the wife of fellow Black Order member Corvus Glaive. Like Glaive, she is a warrior, with her preferred weapon being a giant spear created from a star in a trapped quantum singularity. Proxima has worked hard to prove herself worthy in Thanos' eyes, and is sensitive to being seen as lesser than fellow members of the Black Order. She is unwaveringly loyal to Thanos and takes a perverse satisfaction in her violent and brutal work.

BLACK DWARF
BLACK DWARF

POWERS

Incredibly strong. Incredibly tough. Unbreakable skin.

ORIGINS

Every super team needs its powerhouse, and Black Dwarf is the strongest member of the Black Order. Like the stellar remnant from which he takes his name, Black Dwarf is super dense, very strong and impenetrably tough. Black Dwarf's brute power is easily on a level with the strongest of the Earth's mightiest heroes, but as with the rest of the Black Order his weakness comes from his overconfidence – no-one in the Black Order can ever believe that they could be beaten by someone from Earth, and that is always their undoing.

YONDU UDONTA
YONDU

POWERS

Bow with Yaka arrows.

ORIGINS

The outskirts of space can be a pretty dangerous place, and space pirates like Yondu and his band of Ravagers make it even more so. Yondu is a master archer and carries a bow and quiver of Yaka arrows, which he can change the direction of in midair simply by whistling. Despite being a tough pirate, Yondu has a sentimental side – years ago Yondu found a young NASA pilot called Peter Quill stranded in space, and after Quill tried to steal his ship, Yondu let Quill join the crew.

VANCE ASTROVIK
MAJOR VICTORY

POWERS

Captain America's shield. Combat training. Leader and strategist.

Major Victory weilds a time-displaced version of Captain America's shield as a symbol of resistance.

ORIGINS

There are two teams that have taken the name Guardians of the Galaxy – Star-Lord's Guardians and the team from an alternate version of the 31st century. Vance Astrovik is a modern-day astronaut who travelled to the future, where mankind is under attack by a vicious alien race called the Badoon. Vance took the name Major Victory and founded the 31st Century Guardians of the Galaxy. He has since travelled back in time to the present day, and the multiple versions of Vance in different timelines are quite the paradox.

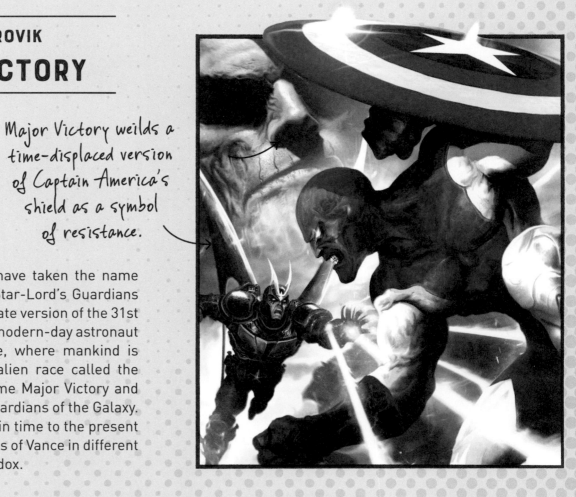

RICHARD RIDER, SAM ALEXANDER
NOVA

POWERS

Flight. Super strength, speed and durability. Energy absorption/redirection.

ORIGINS

The Nova Corps are the elite police corps of the planet Xandar. They take their power from the Nova Force which is managed by their distinctive uniforms. Earth native Richard Rider was given the uniform by a dying alien and for years he thought he was the last of the Nova Corps, until the Corps were reformed to patrol the galaxy. When Richard Rider was thought dead in the line of duty, a new Nova called Sam Alexander was chosen. Now both Sam and Richard patrol space together.

The Nova suit grants a range of energy-based powers.

ADAM WARLOCK
ADAM WARLOCK

POWERS

Flight. Superhuman strength, durability. Energy manipulation.

Adam Warlock was meant to be the perfect man, but even he couldn't handle the power of the Infinity Stones.

ORIGINS

An artificial man, created by Earth scientists to be the perfect human being, Adam Warlock rebelled against his creators and tried to bring good to the universe. Adam became a cosmic being, the protector of the powerful Infinity Stones and the bearer of the Soul Stone. Thanos has been one of his greatest opponents, since he will stop at nothing to acquire the Infinity Stones. The team that Adam Warlock formed to protect the Infinity Stones was called the Infinity Watch, and Adam has since worked with Star-Lord's Guardians of the Galaxy.

EGO

EGO, THE LIVING PLANET

POWERS

Psychic powers. Matter manipulation. Planet.

ORIGINS

Some villains are bigger than others, and they don't come much bigger than Ego, the living planet. Ego is a planet who developed consciousness as well as the ability to control its own mass down to a molecular level, reshaping its surface to fight off invaders. As a sentient planet, Ego needs food, and it consumes spaceships and other planets to survive. Once it even set its sights on Earth, but it was stopped by Earth's heroes.

Ego was not created in our galaxy, but fled from the Black Galaxy.

J'SON OF SPARTAX

J'SON

POWERS

Combat training.

The Spartax have tried to sacrifice Earth in the past.

ORIGINS

Peter Quill's father is the king of the Spartax planetary system, and a member of the Galactic Council. He is a proud and sometimes arrogant man who wants his son to leave the Guardians of the Galaxy and join him ruling Spartax. J'son does not share his son's belief in the sanctity of life, and will kill and destroy to get what he wants, regardless of who gets in the way. Despite his son being half human, J'Son has absolutely no warm feelings for anyone from Earth.

BLASTAAR

BLASTAAR

POWERS

Superhuman strength, stamina. Energy blasts. Flight.

ORIGINS

A Baluurian from the Negative Zone, Blastaar was the ruler of his race until they deposed him for his cruelty and brutality. He left the Negative Zone and for a while tried to conquer Earth, but was beaten back by Earth's heroes. Blastaar has since decided that he should be king of the Kree and has been fighting hard for this position. Blastaar has helped the galaxy's heroes when it is in his self-interest, but cannot be counted on not to betray his allies.

ADAM WARLOCK

MAGUS

POWERS

Flight. Superhuman strength, durability. Energy manipulation.

ORIGINS

The evil Magus is actually a corrupted version of Adam Warlock from the future, who created a religious empire called the Universal Church of Truth. Adam Warlock has been able to change his timeline so that he will never become the Magus, but the Magus keeps returning to battle Adam and remind him of his own worst instincts. The Magus is such an important threat that arch-enemies Adam Warlock and Thanos have been forced to team up to stop him.

Magnus also desires the power of the Infinity Stones. →

NORRIN RADD

SILVER SURFER

POWERS

Power Cosmic. Cosmic surfboard.

ORIGINS

Norrin Radd was given a choice by Galactus – either watch Galactus consume his home planet of Zenn-La or act as his herald, leading the way to find more planets to devour. Norrin was imbued with the Power Cosmic, transforming him into the Silver Surfer. When the Silver Surfer visited Earth the Fantastic Four convinced him to help them against Galactus and he turned on his former master. The Silver Surfer now travels the galaxy looking to atone for his actions as Galactus' herald.

The Silver Surfer's board is called Toome.

KALLARK

GLADIATOR

POWERS

Flight. Super strength, speed and durability.

ORIGINS

Gladiator is the leader of the Shi'ar Imperial Guard, and is honour-bound to serve whoever sits on the Shi'ar throne. He is at the upper limit of superhuman strength, and can shatter planets with his blows. Gladiator has been an ally to the X-Men, Fantastic Four and other Earth heroes, but his ultimate allegiance lies with the Shi'ar Empire. Despite being only the size of a human, Gladiator is perfectly capable of keeping entire galactic armies at bay.

WENDELL VAUGHN

QUASAR

POWERS

Quantum Bands grant flight, super strength and speed, quantum energy.

The power from the Quantum Bands is like nothing else in the universe.

ORIGINS

Quasar wields the cosmic Quantum Bands, which allow the wearer to manipulate quantum energy in complex and physical forms. Wendell Vaughn from Earth was the first hero to take the name Quasar, using the power of the bands to protect the universe from his base on Earth. Vaughn's bravery, selflessness and determination make him the ideal bearer of one of the most powerful weapons in the universe. The Quantum Bands have been used by others, but always seem to return to Wendell Vaughn somehow.

EROS OF TITAN

STARFOX

POWERS

Psychic control of others' emotions. Flight. Super strength and stamina.

ORIGINS

Thanos' brother is absolutely nothing like him at all. While the mad Titan only cares about death, Eros is far more interested in the living, and enjoys using his natural psychic powers to induce pleasure in others. Eros spent years as a cosmic gadabout and adventurer, before taking arms against his brother when Thanos attacked their homeworld of Titan. Longing for adventure, he joined the Avengers on Earth, where he was given the name Starfox.

GALAN
GALACTUS

POWERS

Eats planets. Controls the Power Cosmic.

ORIGINS

Galactus was alive before the birth of our universe, and he will be one of the last beings alive when it ends. A giant, god-like presence, Galactus' true form cannot be seen by most beings – all they see is a giant version of their own species. Feared throughout the universe, Galactus uses the Power Cosmic, a nearly limitless cosmic energy. Although he is unimaginably powerful, Galactus needs to devour planets to survive and sends his heralds out through the universe to find his next meal.

Reed Richards managed to scare Galactus from Earth by threatening him with the Ultimate Nullifier.

TYROS
TERRAX

POWERS

Imbued with the Power Cosmic. Flight. Super strength and stamina. Earth manipulation.

Many of the former Heralds of Galactus still have incredible powers.

ORIGINS

Being a Herald of Galactus suits a certain type of personality, and Terrax was very, very good at it, finding more planets than any other herald. Terrax was never fully loyal to his master, and instead used his powers for personal gain – he conquered planets in his own name and set himself up as a god. When Galactus found out, Terrax hid in a black hole, but was eventually found and punished. Terrax is still a heavy hitter, but the Power Cosmic within him has been reduced.

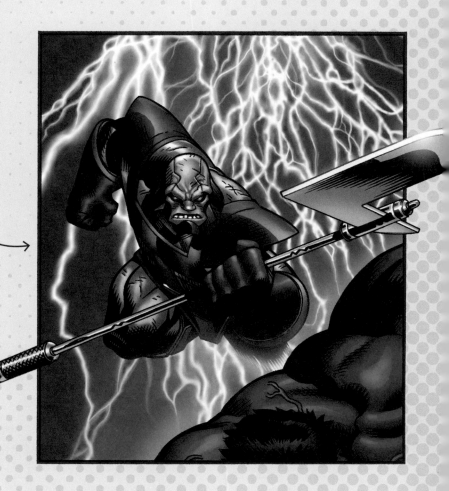

UATU
UATU THE WATCHER

POWERS

Cosmic powers.
Superhuman intelligence.

The appearance of a Watcher normally means something important is about to happen.

ORIGINS

Neither a hero nor a villain, Uatu is a member of the Watchers, an alien race who are sworn to observe and not meddle in the affairs of other species. Uatu was assigned to watch Earth from his base on our moon, and appears at pivotal moments in Earth's history to see events unfold. Although he is not allowed to interfere, Uatu has helped Earth heroes on occasion and has been reprimanded by other Watchers for this. Uatu can see current situations, and look into the multiverse to see what might have been, had events occurred differently. Uatu was killed by Nick Fury Snr, the former Director of S.H.I.E.L.D. who now takes his place on the moon, observing the multiverse.

TANELEER TIVAN
COLLECTOR

POWERS

Power Primordial allows him to do almost anything.
Immortal.

ORIGINS

An Elder of the Universe, like the Grandmaster, the Collector is utterly obsessed with collecting objects and life forms that he thinks are valuable. Taneleer Tivan has been alive for billions of years and has mastered the Power Primordial, making him enormously powerful. He has tried to collect many super heroes as specimens, especially the Avengers, but has always been stopped. The Collector has a vast collection of weapons, guards and traps that he can use to acquire and detain anything or anyone that he wants in his collection.

CHAPTER TEN

DOCTOR STRANGE
AND THE SUPERNATURAL

NICK FURY'S NOTES

There are some things that I will never understand, but if they threaten the Earth then I need to know how to stop them. Stephen Strange sees across vast dimensions that I can only imagine, tracking threats that could end existence as we know it.

This is the sort of thing that keeps me up at night. I'm not worried about crazed super villains trying to take over the world or rampaging aliens from another planet, it's the giant multi-dimensional beings that scare me. I just hope Strange knows what he's doing.

STEPHEN STRANGE

DOCTOR STRANGE

POWERS

Sorcerer Supreme. Cloak of Levitation.
Eye of Agamotto.

Doctor Strange can be found in New York, on Bleecker Street.

ORIGINS

Shallow and egotistical surgeon Doctor Stephen Strange was in a car accident which severely damaged his hands. It took away his ability to perform surgery, which was the most important thing is his life. Stephen's search to heal his hands brought him to the Ancient One, who trained Stephen in the ways of magic. Now Doctor Strange is the Sorcerer Supreme, Earth's foremost protector against magical and mystical threats. Doctor Strange draws his powers from a range of mystical entities and casts spells from the Book of the Vishanti.

WONG

WONG

POWERS

Martial arts training. Mystic arts mastery.

ORIGINS

Doctor Strange lives in the mystic Sanctum Santorum in New York City with his friend and servant, Wong. Born in the mystical city of Kamar-Taj, Wong was originally sent by the Ancient One to learn from Strange, and though he is not the Sorcerer that Doctor Strange is, Wong has learned a lot from his master. He is also extremely adept in martial arts, and can take on many foes at the same time in unarmed combat. Wong is an invaluable and trusted ally and confidant to Doctor Strange, and knows the Sorcerer Supreme perhaps better than anyone else on Earth.

UNKNOWN
THE ANCIENT ONE

POWERS

Magic. Teleportation.

ORIGINS

The Ancient One was the Sorcerer Supreme before passing the title on to his student, Doctor Strange. Once a humble farmer in the Himalayan Mountains, he discovered how to use magic and travelled the world, collecting magic items. The Ancient One returned to his home city of Kamar-Taj, transforming it into a bastion of magical study and mystical contemplation. He trained many, including Baron Mordo, but only Stephen Strange was fit to succeed him as the Sorcerer Supreme.

CLEA
CLEA

POWERS

Training in the mystic arts.

Clea is perhaps Stephen Strange's greatest weakness.

ORIGINS

Clea is a former student and also former romantic partner of Doctor Strange. She is a member of the Faltine race and comes from the Dark Dimension, where she lead the fight against her uncle, Dormammu. Clea is the Sorceress Supreme of the Dark Dimension and has access to a vast range of magical knowledge and raw magical power that rivals anyone on Earth. Although Clea is the rightful ruler of the Dark Dimension she was usurped by Dormammu, and travels the multiverse looking for a home.

KARL MORDO
BARON MORDO

POWERS

Extensive study of Black Magic.

ORIGINS

Stephen Strange was not the only pupil of the Ancient One. Baron Mordo grew frustrated with his master and conspired to kill him, but Strange became aware of his plot and tried to stop him. Mordo was exiled by the Ancient One, blaming Doctor Strange for his predicament. Over the years Mordo has delved deeper and deeper into black magic, conspiring with foes such as Dormammu and Mephisto to give him an advantage against Strange. Although it has given him a wide range of powers, this reliance on the dark arts has twisted Baron Mordu, making him bitter and evil.

DORMAMMU
DORMAMMU

POWERS

Master of dark magic. Interdimensional energy and matter manipulation.

Dormammu is always at the edge of the Dark Dimension, waiting to take over our world.

ORIGINS

It's hard for human minds to comprehend an ancient and limitless evil like Dormammu. Dormammu only cares about conquest, and is constantly looking for more dimensions and planes of existence to bend to his will. Dormammu is an interdimensional being of energy, chaos and malevolence. His power is vast and it has tested Doctor Strange to his limits to beat back Dormammu time and time again, banishing him to the Dark Dimension where he rules.

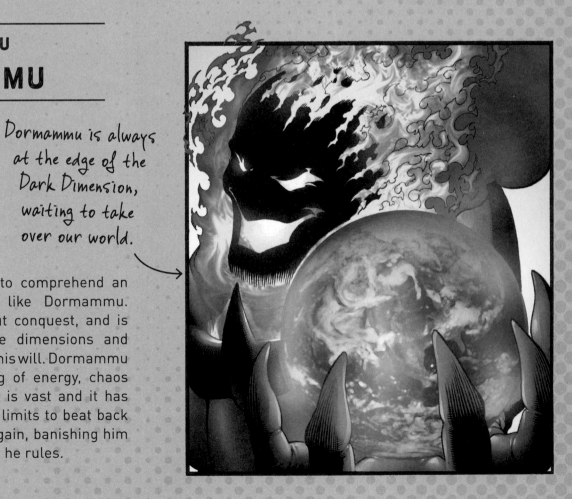

MEPHISTO
MEPHISTO

POWERS

Dark magic. Immortality.

Under no circumstances make a deal with Mephisto.

ORIGINS

Mephisto loves nothing more than making bargains with people who are at their lowest point. The Hell-lord ruler of a fiery afterlife dimension, he offers much but never delivers exactly what he seems to promise. Mephisto was the one who bargained for Johnny Blaze's soul, turning him into Ghost Rider by bonding him with a demon. Mephisto has a son called Blackheart, a being created from pure evil. Although he commands a range of demons Mephisto is constantly looking for more power and trying to expand the boundaries of his dimension. He is NOT to be trusted.

NIGHTMARE
NIGHTMARE

POWERS

Power over dreaming beings. Near omnipotence in his own dimension.

ORIGINS

You've met Nightmare before, just not when you were awake. The ruler of the Dream Dimension, Nightmare plays in humanity's collective unconscious, feeding on our psychic energy while we sleep. Nightmare will torture dreamers for his own amusement and has sent heroes like Hulk into mindless rampages. Doctor Strange is the Earth's foremost protector against Nightmare, freeing those who are imprisoned in his dimension and helping the rest of us sleep a little sounder.

JOHNNY BLAZE.
DANNY KETCH. ROBBIE REYES.
GHOST RIDER

POWERS

Superhuman strength, stamina.
Penance stare. Flaming
vehicles.

The first Rider was on the Earth a million years ago.

ORIGINS

The Ghost Rider is a mystical figure – a curse that has followed humanity for thousands of years with many different people taking on the role. Motorcycle stuntman Johnny Blaze became the Ghost Rider when he sold his soul to a Hell-Lord. Blaze's brother Danny Ketch became Ghost Rider when he touched the hubcap of a mystic motorcycle. The current Ghost Rider is Robbie Reyes, and he drives a car instead of a motorcycle. All Ghost Riders have access to the Penance Stare, which forces the victim to experience all the pain and suffering they have inflicted on others.

ERIC BROOKS
BLADE

POWERS

Martial arts.
Superhuman strength,
speed and stamina.
Enhanced senses.

Blade has had years to perfect the art of armed and unarmed combat.

ORIGINS

Born in London in the 1920s, Eric Brooks was given superhuman powers when a vampire bit his mother during labour. Blade is neither a vampire nor a human, but something in between. He has dedicated his existence to hunting down and eradicating vampires and he has even fought Dracula himself many times over the years. Blade is known by vampires as the Daywalker. He possesses most vampire strengths but he does not suffer their weakness to sunlight.

DOCTOR MICHAEL MORBIUS
MORBIUS, THE LIVING VAMPIRE

POWERS

Superhuman strength, speed and stamina. Flight. Hypnotism.

ORIGINS

Unlike other vampires, Morbius is a synthetic vampire whose condition is the result of a medical experiment. Biochemist Dr. Michael Morbius was dying from a blood disorder, so he gave himself a serum taken from bat's blood which changed his physiology forever. Morbius now had superhuman abilities, but they came with an insatiable thirst for blood and an aversion to light. He was initially a villain, fighting Spider-Man and the X-Men, but has since vowed to only drink the blood of the guilty.

SHANG-CHI
SHANG-CHI: MASTER OF KUNG FU

POWERS

Master martial artist.

ORIGINS

Is Shang-Chi the greatest unarmed fighter in the world? Many heroes, villains and gods think so. Trained in the martial arts since birth, he mastered countless forms of combat under the tutelage of his criminal mastermind father. Shang-Chi was sent to London to assassinate an enemy of his father, but instead learned of his father's evil empire and renounced him. He travelled the world and became a hero, using his incredible abilities to help the innocent. Shang-Chi has trained Spider-Man and other heroes in Kung Fu, and has been an important member of the Avengers.

CHAPTER ELEVEN
THE NEW GENERATION

NICK FURY'S NOTES

We all need to start somewhere.

It gives me hope when I see the new generation of heroes. These are bright, positive kids who want to do the right thing. They work together to make the world a better place, and there's something inspiring about seeing them be the change that they want to be in the world.

They are hopeful, brave and idealistic – they haven't become cold, cynical and pragmatic yet. I guess that's because being cynical and pragmatic is my job...

RIRI WILLIAMS
IRONHEART

POWERS

Scientific genius.
Suit of cutting-edge
armour.

Ironheart's armour has an AI version of Tony Stark to advise her.

ORIGINS

Inspired by the exploits of Tony Stark, teenage genius Riri Williams reverse-engineered Starktech to create her own incredibly advanced suit of armour. As Ironheart she spends her time fighting to protect the world from hi-tech villains and monsters, while trying to keep her family safe at the same time. Although she is lacking in experience (sometimes to a dangerous degree), she more than makes up for it with her bravery, intelligence, heart and determination.

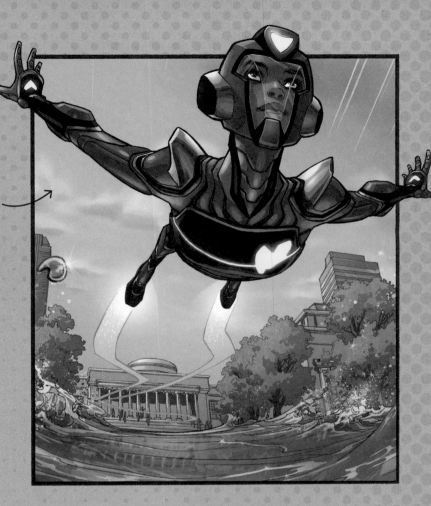

Miles Morales grew up in a slightly different universe than our own.

MILES MORALES
SPIDER-MAN

POWERS

Increased strength, reflexes, stamina and agility. Can shoot bio-electric blasts. Sticks to walls. Wrist-mounted mechanical web shooters.

ORIGINS

Miles got his powers when he was bitten by a spider that was meant to replicate Peter Parker's abilities. Miles has slightly different powers to Peter, and can produce a type of blast which he calls his 'venom strike' and uses to knock out his enemies. Miles is much younger than Peter and still has a great deal to learn – he hasn't quite got used to juggling his super hero life with his school work and pressure from his parents. Despite his youth, Miles is every bit as much a hero as Peter Parker.

KAMALA KHAN
MS MARVEL

POWERS

Shapeshifting.
Healing factor.

Kamala Khan writes fan fiction about super heroes in her spare time.

ORIGINS

Young Kamala Khan is one of the biggest super hero fans in the world, so it makes sense that when she got super powers she would become a hero too. Transformed by the Inhumans' Terrigen Mists, she can embiggen different body parts at will. Ms Marvel is bold, idealistic and eager to do the right thing, even if the super hero world can be a confusing place sometimes. Ms Marvel was given her super hero name by her idol and mentor, Carol Danvers, and does her best to uphold the Marvel legacy.

AMADEUS CHO
BRAWN

POWERS

Super genius. Hulk-level strength

ORIGINS

One of the smartest people on the planet, teenager Amadeus Cho dedicated himself to helping the Hulk, who he realised was misunderstood. When Banner absorbed a lethal amount of radiation, Amadeus Cho used special nanites to absorb it, transforming into a version of the Hulk. Cho is now brilliantly clever and also incredibly strong, but he struggles with the darker, repressed side of being a Hulk. Calling himself Brawn, he has joined the teen super hero group, The Champions, providing brains and muscle.

DOREEN GREEN
SQUIRREL GIRL

POWERS

Prehensile tail. Superhuman sense and strength. Can talk to squirrels.

ORIGINS

Squirrel Girl might not look too dangerous, but she has gone up against some of the heaviest hitters in the universe, including Doctor Doom, Galactus and even Thanos. Born with a prehensile tail, enhanced strength and the ability to talk to squirrels, Doreen Green fights crime with her squirrel companion, Tippy-Toe. In an age when super heroes are often cynical and bitter, Squirrel Girl stands out by being almost relentlessly upbeat, bringing a smile and a happy word to all super hero confontations.

LAURA KINNEY
X-23

POWERS

Heightened senses. Healing factor. Adamantium claws in hands and feet.

Like Logan, Laura Kinney has adamantium bones.

ORIGINS

Wolverine was always too effective for there to be just one of him, so a group called the Facility created a female clone from his DNA. X-23 was designed to be the perfect killing machine, and she was a highly effective assassin before she escaped her training. Since then, Wolverine has taken her in and adopted her. Under the name Laura Kinney, she enrolled in the Xavier Institute and now uses her claws, healing factor and combat training for good as a member of the X-Men.

LUNELLA LAFAYETTE/DINOSAUR
MOON GIRL
AND DEVIL DINOSAUR

POWERS

Top-level super genius. Consciousness transferral.

ORIGINS

Lunella Lafayette is the smartest person in the world, even though she is only nine years old. Devil Dinosaur is a giant, red dinosaur who is very good at stomping on things. The two are best friends and have a telepathic link – they can transfer consciousness between bodies, but this tends to happen when Lunella is angry or very hungry. Part of Moon Girl's genius means that she tries to understand those who are misunderstood, and the two friends will always fight for what is right.

KATE BISHOP
HAWKEYE

POWERS

Top-level marksmanship. Exceptional at hand-to-hand combat and sword fighting.

Both Kate Bishop and Clint Barton claim that they are the superior archer.

ORIGINS

Clint Barton has been mentoring Kate Bishop to be a hero, and the two share the Hawkeye name at the same time. Kate comes from a wealthy family, but after she found out that her father was a criminal she rejected his money and trained hard to become a hero. She is as good an archer as Clint and is skilled with a variety of weapons. Eventually Kate became frustrated with Clint's haphazard teaching style, so she moved to Los Angeles and became a private investigator and hero-for-hire.